THE DOLPHIN PROJECT

To those who feel they need a complete relationship . . .

By

Michael Marlan

Canadian Cataloguing in Publication Data

Marlan, Michael.
  The dolphin project

  ISBN 0-929096-00-2

  I. Title.
  PS8576.A75D6 1989   C813'.54   C89-091358-7
  PR9199.3.M37D6 1989

THE DOLPHIN PROJECT

By
Michael Marlan

Published By
Sunspring Publishing Company
P.O. Box 858
Raymond, Alberta Canada T0K 2S0

ISBN 0-929096-00-2

Printed in Canada
Copyright 1989 Sunspring Raymond, Alberta

"Thus saith the Lord: Ye are gods and children of the Most High." Psalm 82:6

PROLOGUE

Marlan and Kira had been inseparable. Children of a god, in light bodies they had danced together among the stars for eons of time. The old gods had beamed with joy as this eternal dyad from the star system Kobol had flashed from planet to planet, ring to ring, system to system. Alive with light, joy, wonder, they had carried within them the rainbow spectrum and the heartsong that bid them and their festival of light welcome, and safe passage to anywhere in time.

Yet even in those carefree innocent moments together, moments that on a planet like Earth would span millions of years in time, they had both known that one day they would need to create a space of their very own. Only then, in the dominion of their own space and time, could they consummate their love and create their own children, their own new dyads, from the endless sea of infinite elemental intelligence that they knew filled all space.

This deep inner knowing, this knowledge that they would have to master gross matter in order to create their own worlds, is itself the restless foreboding that gradually weighed down the light bodies of Marlan and Kira. It had forced them to become slow in their movements, clumsy in communication, and to descend into physical substance.

Gradually the lightning had ceased to flow through their veins; their heartsong had changed with the doubting. No longer were they welcome and safe to pass through all systems. Their coarse vibrations would have been destructive to the fine spirit creations among which they had played. Marlan and Kira had begun to know sadness, loneliness, separation. Instead of pure joy, they had begun to know love.

As they descended, their love had been felt in many systems as an ever present tension, as an ebb and a flow, as a muted sound like the throb of some distant mystic drum in the stillness of a perfect night. There were sensitives on many planets who recorded at the time of the separation of Marlan and Kira, that somewhere a god was weeping.

II.

Marlan was alone on Mu. He had chosen to remain behind to complete the record of his people, and to prepare a way for their return perhaps many thousands or millions of earth years later. He knew that his work, the dolphin project, must be completed to perfection.

The aging process in Marlan's physical body had been altered. As he moved his fingers through his long flowing golden hair, he remembered how exciting it had been when word had gone out from the temples that the secrets of perpetual youth had been restored to Lemuria.

He remembered too the confusion the announcement had caused in the health professions, and the economic sector. Somewhere, he thought, some hidden governing council must have labored hard to reach a decision to share temple secrets with the people.

Marlan and Kira had been chosen among the first to be called to the temple. They hadn't really known why they had been chosen except that they had kept the laws of the land and given loving service to others. From the time of their first introduction, Marlan and Kira each knew that they had known the other long before. They also shared a secret feeling that they would one day be called to a great work.

As Marlan waited for the dolphins to return, he admired again the perfect form of his naked hands and arms. He felt the throb of power that constantly pulsed through his muscles and sinews. His was a perfect body, a body like that of the gods.

But Marlan was lonely. He thought often of Kira who had left years before with the last remnants of their people, for new homes among the seven stars. His mind scanned the centuries and retrieved the memory of how it had been when he and Kira had first entered the temple.

They were instructed to leave everything behind, to bring only the clothing they wore. It was a glorious morning, a magic morning from the very moment they left their home and saw the birds fly strangely, circling and calling softly above their heads. They walked hand in hand with peace in their hearts, and a strange composure settling upon their lips and countenance. Those who peeked out of their windows and saw them would say later that already Marlan and Kira had been transformed.

From the outside courtyard, the inner doors of the temple appeared to be as a polished sea of glass, spun perhaps from pure gold. They noted their reflection and saw that the sands of time had marked them in their mature years; matching wrinkle for wrinkle, contour for contour, form for form. They appeared to each other as identical twins; one male, one female.

Never before had Marlan and Kira felt such a completeness of love for each other. The grip of their hands clasped tighter, forming a sphere, a perfect sphere. They passed through the inner doors of the temple.

Some clocks would mark the time they remained inside as six hours, others as six days. Ancient legends would later speak of a temple and an entire city that had risen up to the heavens and disappeared completely from the face of the earth. But for Marlan and Kira time had ceased to exist. . .

The clear crystal sound of the dolphins' light chatter brought Marlan's reluctant thoughts back to the here and now of physical awareness. He knew the dolphins were returning through the underground streams to his retreat deep inside a mountain. They would be well fed from the teeming waters of the warm tropical seas that were slowly swallowing the landform of Lemuria; Mu as it had been affectionately called.

For hundreds of years, the people of Mu had been forced to live in caves with narrow entrances to protect themselves from the giant beasts that had risen up upon the lands after the cataclysm on Atlantis.

Atlantis was the other wing of the sacred eagle. The eagle, an ancient symbol of wisdom, was the shape of certain landforms known among the stars.

Lemuria was the continent that developed the intuitive spiritual parts of man. On Atlantis, souls incarnated to learn about technology, the forces of gross matter and physical manifestation. Atlantis was to ensnare, to weigh down. Lemuria existed to channel the higher desires, to lift up again.

Between the two continents was a landform known as the center. For thousands of earth years, by consent of the rulers of both governing continents, the center was held in reverence and awe as a sacred land upon which only the gods and their apprentices, the initiates of the sacred brotherhoods and priesthoods, could dwell.

For as long as the center was held sacred, the powers developing on the two continents remained in balance. Communication was maintained though special temples governed by the secret priesthood rings. The people were content for things to remain that way. Life was pleasant and good on Mu.

Only much later, just before the cataclysm, had the people any forewarning that something unusual had entered their world. They began to catch glimpses of strange lights in the sky; much higher up and faster moving than the common airships from Atlantis.

They had become accustomed to the peculiar white-blue glow that surrounded the temples which only the priesthoods and their initiates could enter. But they began to hear rumors of people disappearing from their homes, never to be heard from again. There were strange stories of others who had been taken inside wondrous flying machines where they had been interviewed, probed, and examined by people who looked like gods.

There were also the healers, the teachers, the masters of matter who came out from the temples. They seemed to defy all known physical laws. They spoke of a marvelous work and a wonder about to happen among the people.

Now, as Marlan indulged his loneliness, he was aware that Kira, even though physically many light years away, was sharing these memories with him. Their training in the temple had brought them to an awareness that they had a special communication channel of their very own. This channel, when they so desired, could not be tapped by any other organized lifeform, except by a god of a higher order than they.

Marlan felt close to Kira. Their minds melded often. But he wanted to be in her physical presence. He wanted to hold her tight in his arms; to press her body close to his yearning bosom; to gently stroke her soft golden hair, look into her eyes and say, *"I love you Kira!"* He wanted to comfort her now in their separation, and to assure her that again they would be together. In their loneliness for each other, it seemed a very rough game, this game the gods played to become themselves!

Together, Marlan and Kira shared a magic language that formed the completeness of their eternal relationship. Nothing could approach the joy of watching Kira move. Every little motion of her body awakened waves of shared memories. Each tiny lift of an eyelash, each infinitesimal movement of her lips, each tiny quaver in her voice, brought back an ocean of associations, a sea of memories of endless other times in numberless other worlds when she had moved in exactly that same manner before; when she had spoken with precisely that one single haunting sound. . .

III.

Moving effortlessly though the streams deep within the mountains, the dolphins homed in on Marlan's thoughts. They flashed excited messages to each other, wondering what the young god would teach them today. The dolphins were pleased to be a vital part of Marlan's project.

Slowly, inexorably, a deep rumble began within Marlan's powerful chest. As the trembling rose it was shaped into a stream of sound that passed through his open lips; a sound that would have been heard from afar as the sound of the rushing of many waters; but there was no human left to hear. . .

INTRODUCTION

"Our birth is but a sleep and a forgetting: The Soul that rises with us, our life's Star, Hath had elsewhere its setting, And cometh from afar: Not in entire forgetfulness, And not in utter nakedness, But trailing clouds of glory do we come From God, who is our home . . ." William Woodsworth

I first met Marlan in 1984. I was selling life insurance on Vancouver Island at the time. I had rented an apartment in Victoria and was keeping an eye open for some good used furniture.

Well, I must have passed the place a dozen times before, but this one time I was walking along Gorge Road, just past the lumber yard, when I noticed an old building in an otherwise vacant field.

Two things immediately drew my full attention that way. In front of the building was a display of used furniture set out on the grass. The second thing was a huge sign that read: UFO FURNITURE.

I was intrigued to say the least. I thought it might have meant something like Used Furniture Outdoors, or maybe Used Furniture Office. But I was in the market for furniture, so I crossed the street.

As I got closer, I noticed a smaller sign in the parking lot. The sign was obviously handmade. In bright red letters it proclaimed: UFO PARKING.

As I pondered that one, I suddenly realized that one of the old chairs on the lawn was occupied. There was a man seated in it, dressed in clothing that matched the shabby furniture. His head was down so I could not see his eyes. I noticed that his hair was long, clean, and neatly combed. This was quite unlike the norm for people who dressed that way in Victoria. The man's shoulders were massive, his neck and arms unusually thick and muscular, his hands clasped together on his lap. There seemed to be a peculiar white-blue glow surrounding him.

Thinking he was the proprietor, I approached him and said, *"Do you mind if I have a look around?"*

"Hello Paul," the man said, calling me by my first name.

I never did question how he knew my name. His voice sounded totally familiar. Almost as if it was a voice I had heard every day, or my own voice even! I felt like I had known this man all my life, like we were twins and had shared the same experiences.

In broad daylight, I was completely disoriented. It was as though I'd had a sudden stroke. The subconscious voices and myriad meaningless images that had been a seldom-noticed part of my mind as long as I can remember, suddenly stilled and focused as I sat down on the chair he offered.

And then, as the man I came to know by the name of Marlan slowly lifted his head and looked full at me, time ceased to exist. I felt as though I had been wafted away on the wings of some giant bird, and had been set down, gently floating on a soft warm sea. I seemed to hear the distant throb of a great muffled heartbeat. A complete peace filled my being. I was safe, folded in the bosom of eternity. I rested full in the limitless depths of Marlan's magnificent eyes. . .

Chapter One

"The Universe should be deemed an immense Being, always living, always moved and always moving in an eternal activity inherent in itself, and which, subordinate to no foreign cause, is communicated to all its parts, connects them together, and makes the world of things a complete and perfect whole." Albert Pike, 1809-1891

"The hurt of one is the hurt of all; the joy of one is the joy of all." Sioux Educator

"Is it not written in your law, I said, Ye are gods?" John 10:34

Kira and I have returned. By earthdate as I write this record, it is the year 1984 AD. We move within physical form and the world turns for us. As I write, I am located within a power spot on the Pacific-Northwest triangle, in the continent of North America.

The Americas of today, shaped like the eagle's wings, are the remnants of the landforms we knew as the center. They remain sacred lands to us. As Kira and I walk upon this footstool of the gods, we feel as though we should remove our shoes. In the center, we stand upon the holy land where human life began on this planet, and from where it spread out to populate many other worlds. The extraterrestrials who come in what are perceived to be unidentified flying objects, in many cases have had their origins at this very center.

I am Marlan of the dolphin project. The names of the gods describe their attributes and accomplishments. I have many names. In this world, I am Michael Marlan, for I am both priest and king. When I left the dolphins of Mu, I had been trained as a high priest of the most ancient order. From there I went out among the stars and fought a goodly fight throughout many systems. Awake and aware, I became in my own right, a king, a grand master and teacher of the lifeforce at all levels of being.

Kira too has many names and many accomplishments. Yet I shall say little of such. On planets of this order, it is considered irreverent to speak much of the female side of the gods, except in old tales and legends. It is absurd to us to think of a God having children except that God is an eternal dyad, both male and female energies.

The stronger male energies, trained to larger movements, sometimes need to be balanced with a greater counterpart than is found in a single female form. Thus it is said that there are seven sisters in the Pleiades, and that one God may be a father and several mothers.

There are many gods among the stars. Always there is to every god a greater god. Throughout this record I shall write god with a small letter *"g"*, signifying an advanced consciousness, a grand master of the hierarchy, who is god over a limited stewardship or ring of power and responsibility. In those instances where I capitalize the letter *"g"* and write *"God"*, I am referring to those greater gods who have earned the right to create their own space, their own star systems, and to populate those systems with their own increase.

A God's increase are the spirit offspring formed in their own image and likeness from the endless source of elemental intelligence that is the primeval sea from which all lifeforms have evolved. A God is a father/mother relationship and is God with a capital *"G"* only to their own spirit increase.

As new Gods create their own space, all Gods of a higher order advance in the quality of their consciousness and intelligence. They are able to express themselves through that many more organized lifeforms.

All minds are linked as one through their common origin in the sea of elemental intelligence that permeates all space. All lifeforms are coeternal. They have always existed. There is not a tiny movement, a single thought, a little desire anywhere in the universe that is not felt by everything else that exists. The very sands upon the seashore pulsate with life that is linked intimately with the lifeforce of the highest of Gods.

Thus it is that the true grand governing order of the universe is love, understanding, and gentle persuasion toward all lifeforms; be they mineral, plant, animal, human, or any other.

Although it is the hand of Marlan who pens this work, it is the mind of both Marlan and Kira whose thoughts are expressed. Therefore I shall often use the word *"we"* rather than *"I"* and you may know that *"we"* are both male and female expressions.

As always, we approach our communications on the physical level with great concern. We know that all human forms are gods in embryo, and that word symbols are magic, having different meanings at different levels of thought.

The dolphins did not understand this when I returned. There was no fault in their programming; but after many generations had passed, superstitions and legends had been added to the pure input they received on Mu. Intelligent minds constantly seek for a logical wholeness, and for the aggrandizement of that which they most closely identify with.

On Mu I taught the dolphins perfectly. They became a living repository, a database of all the knowledge known to the people of Lemuria; and much from Atlantis as well.

We had carefully studied the many varieties of lifeform evolving upon the earth in those dark days of shadow and sudden change. We

9

selected the dolphins because of their efficient capacity for communication with many levels of the human mind; for their advanced intellect, for their willingness to cooperate and be of service to another stream of consciousness; and because we knew that a lifeform from the seas could best survive the upheavals then happening upon the planet.

We did not dare tamper with human form because we knew only too well how low the gods can sink into dense matter, and yet still be moved by the dim memory and tension of needing to be something much greater, and more powerful.

We knew only too well how we needed to cover our tracks and coordinates as we moved among the stars, in order to escape pursuit by, and direct confrontation with those who once had been our friends and associates upon the side of light, and who were now learning on the other wing, the wing of shadow and destruction. Yes, we understood even then, in that stage of our own development, the need for two wings on the sacred eagle.

It is necessary that there be an opposition in all things for learning to take place on the levels of choice. It is necessary to know evil to comprehend good; to know sickness to appreciate health; pain for pleasure, beauty for its lack. It is necessary to become totally, painfully aware of the need to choose what we really want for our own worlds, before we can be trusted with the power to create and to populate our own space.

As the carnal mind of man wrestles with contradictions that logic cannot cope with, it grows heated and consciousness expands to include new faculties and new awareness.

All systems are patterned after a master plan which was had from the beginning. Each system is designed to train new gods. All systems of the order of this planet include the dark worlds of choice wherein the illusion of separation and opposites can be maintained. All systems include the wings or powers identified with good, and with evil.

If you became a God and were trusted with the power of creating and populating your own worlds, knowing that your system must be patterned after the master plan, how could you send down a favored son to be the Christ if you yourself had not already experienced your own Gethsemane, your own crucifixion?

Jesus said that he did only that which he had seen his father do before him. Therein was his power and his sustenance.

How could you exercise a righteous judgement, as your children with their logic failing them would call upon you to do, if you yourself had not in some way already experienced every single experience to the utmost degree that they could have? How could you possibly understand if you too had not been where they were?

10

Think upon it! Think how great, and how terrible must be the training of a new God. As you ponder, weep for yourself. You too are already on the path and many lower kingdoms perhaps even now await your own becoming.

The prophets have witnessed that it is not an easy thing to approach the gods. They know too that the carnal mind of man is nothing, nothing at all!

Chapter Two

Marlan and Kira gave me, Paul Demars, the stories that make up this book or *"record"* as Marlan called it. As I struggle to find a format and style that will be acceptable to a publisher, I am tempted to leave myself out of it completely. However, since I was intimately involved in some of the experiences, I'll break in occasionally. *(You'll know it's me by the use of brackets.)*

I have changed and rearranged words within sentences, sentences within paragraphs, paragraphs within chapters. In some places I have changed nothing. Strangely, it didn't seem to matter much how I rearranged Marlan's words. Many of the chapters could have been placed in front of most any other, and the book would still have retained a logical wholeness.

As it turned out, I actually spent very little earthtime with Marlan and Kira. But the time I did spend with them was precious. I know that the dolphin project is vitally important to the new age.

Marlan writes stories that are interconnected and build one upon the other to convey knowledge at many different levels. The stories are powerful analogies that tap universal subconscious memories. The ending of his record is startling, and incredibly ties everything together. You will find yourself and many of your own most secret thoughts and feelings in these pages.

The idea that man may become like God is new and startling to many people in the western world. The immediate impression is that it belittles God. And yet we call God *"Father"*. Is it not reasonable that we, his children, would be shaped in his image and likeness? Is it not reasonable that we could somehow grow and progress until we are like our heavenly parents? Could not our earth families be patterned after and symbolic of a greater truth?

These are questions I struggled to answer within myself. Man's potential to become as God is, is the core message left by Marlan and Kira. This startling concept is difficult for western man to think upon. Knowing this, Marlan wrote as he did, in thought-provoking analogies that stretch our mortal minds sometimes to their very screeching limits. . .

I have added introductory quotes to many of Marlan's chapters in an attempt to demonstrate that the ideas he is expressing are really not so strange, but have actually been around for a long time. Adding these quotes, I think, is my own greatest contribution to the project. Yet, my hand shakes as I try to pick out the most appropriate from a vast selection!

Many of the quotes are from the bible. Marlan was completely familiar with the bible. He consistently acknowledges a greater god than himself, bears witness of the essential work of Jesus Christ, and identifies the highest God as the literal father of his, and our spirit bodies. In his record he encourages us to study the prophetic scriptures to avoid surprises regarding what is now taking place in our world.

Maybe it's just me, but I think that many people in the western world, especially those who were raised in an orthodox religion as I was, will find much that is novel and hard to accept in these pages. I anticipate that it will be a controversial book, and that it will rub hard against many people's traditional beliefs. The psychologists will likely have a few things to say as well!

Yet, the only constant in our age seems to be change. Marlan once said to me, *"It is written that God is unchanging. If that is so, it is that he has forever been changing!"*

Jesus said that he had come to fulfill, and thus to change, the Mosaic law. Throughout the biblical record, prophets received communications from God that resulted in change. If indeed God is unchanging, then we should expect prophets, ministering angels, revelation, and change to continue in our day.

The idea that God is a formless spirit is understandable in light of Marlan's statement that everything in the universe, including ourselves, has been organized from *"a primeval sea of elemental intelligence"* that has always existed. Perhaps this *"elemental intelligence"*, or universal spirit, is the missing link in orthodox Christian theology.

For me, Marlan's book does not take away from that which I had, but adds to it. It is like a door has opened, letting in fresh air and light!

Marlan teaches that when we are ready, we will receive *"line upon line, precept upon precept."* As we trust enough to walk forward into the dark, the dark disperses as we move, and we see and comprehend more and more of the universe. This is not to say that that which we

13

knew before was not true, but that we can now add to it; and are greater for that added knowledge.

It's sort of like a blind man examining an elephant's leg, and rendering an opinion as to what the creature is like. Could he stand back and look at the whole, not only would his knowledge be complete in that creature's exterior, but he could also harness the elephant to accomplish new ends!

All I can do is urge you, if you were raised as I was, to have a flexible mind. As someone once said: *"Minds are like parachutes; they only function when open!"*

Try to find which character in which story most nearly resembles yourself. Marlan says you are very close when you find yourself with the television set. Above all, make sure once you have started the book, that you read it all the way through!

The Dolphin Project, Marlan's record, is a story of creation. It is the story of man; as he was, as he is, and as he may become. Only you will know for sure what is fantasy, and what is truth. Marlan admits that his writings contain *"trivia"*. But it's there for a purpose. His book, like life itself, has veins of pure ore, and arteries of fools gold. Follow the right path, that which you most love, and you will find the motherlode!

Chapter Three

"You are a distinct portion of the essence of God; and contain part of him in yourself. Why, then, are you ignorant of your noble birth? Why do you not consider whence you came? Why do you not remember, when you are eating, who you are who eat; and whom you feed? Do you not know that it is the Divine you feed; the Divine you exercise? You carry a God about with you, poor wretch, and know nothing of it." Epictetus, A.D. 50

"There be gods many, and lords many." 1 Corinthians 8:5

A word of warning to you who read of Marlan and Kira and who refresh the memory of your own training among the stars. Be warned that in this record, as in all things that you bring into your awareness, you must think and choose carefully that which you will accept for your own learning and philosophical foundation, and that which you would reject. You alone are responsible for how you act within the levels of choice.

It may be that we have deliberately built trivia into this record for the purpose of encouraging you to think and to judge for yourself. These pages are a tool to assist you to think clearly for yourself, and to make your own choices in all things.

Maybe you yourself have already been touched by the master's hand at a higher level; perhaps when your body slept and dreamed. You too may somewhere be suddenly snatched out of time. If you have been marked, accept from us that even though you fear and tremble, your training has been perfect. None are chosen but those who have already somewhere, sometime, made the choice for themselves.

You must become a master of the underworld if you would walk with the Gods in the heavens. They too have worked out their stature with doubt and anxiety, on a world such as this one. Furthermore, it is impossible to stand still. Consciousness must always move when within the choice levels. It either moves in ascending, or descending arcs. The choice of which, is yours.

We cannot speak to you of how exquisite are the joys and the rewards of a complete relationship with the greater gods. Like trying to learn from another in words what salt tastes like, you can only know for sure by partaking of it yourself.

Today is called a day of judgement, a day when the wheat is being separated from the chaff. Even now there may be a ring of forty loosed upon this earth and its environments to separate the sheep from the goats, the legitimate from the illegitimate. We give to you for your consideration some of that which was revealed to us behind the golden door of the temple..

As you think for yourself and make your own clear choices, you can progress rapidly beyond the necessity of being bound further to the dark worlds of illusion. Your mind and understanding will expand, and the veil of forgetfulness will thin, as learning accelerates to supermortal speeds.

At no time are you ever completely left alone as was the Christ in Gethsemane. Always for you there are guides, angels, helps, signs along the way. They are always there, but you yourself must open the door of awareness to let them in.

Remember, mistakes are to be corrected not punished. Forgive yourself first and banish guilt to let confidence and faith in. Prayer, meditation, uplifting thoughts, service to others, reading the best books and pondering their message, a heart full of love; these are sure signs of a god in training.

Should you allow yourself to become complacent or lukewarm by not thinking clearly for yourself, and following up your careful choices with correct action, you will fall asleep as if in a trance. Your life and relationships will be manipulated by external forces as though you were only a puppet on a string.

The levels of choice and illusion are the levels in which the rings of magic, sorcery, witchcraft, operate on both the shadow and the white wings. They operate through lifeforms such as your own.

You may think you are plagued by *"bad luck"*, or offer yourself some other explanation for your circumstances. If you consistently choose not to choose for yourself, others will take delight in choosing for you. They will learn much more rapidly by including your lifeform in their own system of vicarious slaves. You will be for them an extra pair of eyes, and another set of ears, to observe and to manipulate the physical world with.

Chapter Four

"For behold, I create new heavens and a new earth: and the former shall not be remembered, nor come into mind." Isaiah 52:6

"And all the host of heaven shall be dissolved, and the heavens shall be rolled together as a scroll." Isaiah 34:4

"And he shall send Jesus Christ, which before was preached unto you: Whom the heaven must receive until the times of restitution of all things which God hath spoken by the mouth of all his holy prophets since the world began." Acts 3:20,21

"Now I know that the Lord is greater than all gods. . ." Exodus 18:11

Kira and I will not be responsible for the progress of those who are not our own children. We are apprentices yet, and gods with a small *"g"*. We are here as helps, and for our own further training and experience in the splitting of a world.

We move within high rings of power and understanding, yet we too acknowledge the greater burden and responsibility for this planet of an elder brother. We have witnessed this brother's work, and his creations, here and among the stars upon planets as numberless as the grains of sand upon the seashore. Yet we do not wish to mystify him in any way. We do not worship him, we learn from him. Worship, if need be at all, is more appropriate for God.

We understand the confusion that may result in the minds of some as we identify personalties associated with powerful religious concepts. It may be that there are two wings to every religion and belief, as there are two wings to the human brain. Each wing in the world of illusion tends to view itself as being in opposition to the other, and therefore either one or the other is perceived to be correct or incorrect. This causes enmity, confrontation, tension, choices, and delightful opportunities for learning! It also maintains the illusion.

The personality known to the western world as Jesus Christ, promised that he would one day return to this planet. He promised that he would return to restore that which was in the beginning, and to usher in a golden age. This would be an age when time would be no longer fixed; when a child would live to the age of a tree; when disease and death would be no more; when the wolf and the lamb would play together without enmity.

He said that he would not come as a man walking upon the earth, nor as a woman; but in his rightful glory as a king and a god descending in flames of fire from the stars.

The Gods always retain the final balance of power to themselves. They keep the time! In that way a God can ensure that everything is prepared to perfection prior to a giant step being taken in any evolutionary chain. By keeping the timing of such an event to themselves, a perfect balance on a colossal scale can be kept between the forces of matter and antimatter as they operate upon the levels of a star system.

We do not know when new age energies will peak to the point where synergy is reached and a new creation is born. We do expect it to happen suddenly, and to take place only when the final catalyst, the last essential character, appears upon the stage. The timing must be absolutely precise. It cannot allow the slightest error if balance is to be maintained, and the universe is to continue to expand, and not begin to rush back upon itself.

The Gods must exercise a righteous judgement before a world is split and a portion of humanity consigned to a descendent arc as another rises. All choices must be in and recorded.

Again, we warn you to think for yourself clearly and to make correct choices of your own, based on the light and the affirmative programming that is unique to your own inner essence. All are judged according to the laws which they know. You may find yourself in judging yourself.

Kira and I have seen many potentials for this world. Like the stay of the destruction pronounced by Jonah upon the city of Ninevah, there remain many possibilities as long as time and freedom to choose exist.

We know the power of man to change those things he knows are incorrect, and to choose an ascendent course. We know the power that even one individual with initiative can have in influencing the minds of thousands of others. We know the power of love and gentle persuasion. We would by choice talk of peace, and not of destruction.

What if through exercising their freedom to choose, there came to be not a single man or woman upon the earth whose choices indicated their need to go with a lesser world when this one is split? What then of the arc, the ring, the circle of power upon which all physical truth, and all balance is maintained? The witch, the sorcerer, work with rings, circles of power, left or right to construct or destruct. They understand the witches' mirror upon which illusion is founded.

All human relationships become circles upon the earth, affecting the lives of many. That is why at death or judgement some find their lives reviewed completely as the inadvertent magic is undone.

The sorcerer's apprentice begins by making broad sweeps around

18

the objects he is seeking to control. Later, as his faith in the art develops, he may simply make a circular motion above a map, a picture, or even a doll. Perhaps white sorcerers are more humane than modern medicine men who torture the human body instead of using a doll or symbol as a proxy!

The history of the world can become an exceedingly complex maze; an intricate structure of intertwining magical relationships. Separate rings and individuals of magic completely lose touch with the ripples they have sent out, and their effect upon complex relationships.

What of the medical doctor for example, who didn't prepare well enough for surgery and loses a patient? What is the effect upon the patient's children, acquaintances, and generations unborn? What of the counselor, the lawyer who gives poor advice? Who can be accountable for the ripples?

Especially in a time of television and rapid technological communications, when even the densest of carnal minds can be touched directly by thousands; the maze of magic accelerates to supermortal rates and quantities. What god can reach out and undo all that karma? Who is really responsible for what? Who can strike a balance between justice and mercy, sacrifice and being?

The sorcerers know that to undo a right circuit you must make a left circuit. But if you make a left circuit how will it affect the millions of other interlocking circuits that have accumulated with time and magical operations? Logic becomes confounded. The wisdom of the wisemen fails. The computer breaks down.

Only the Gods have the power and the timing to make a whole world spin the other way; or perhaps to wrap it up like a scroll. Only the Gods could turn a vertical ring and lay it flat to remove both ascendent and descendent arcs. Yet even the Gods are bound by the choices of the least of lifeforms. . .

Kira and I have indeed seen many possibilities for this world. But the time draws close when the Gods must act. Everything must be speeded up if anything is to survive the tension. All movements and operations of powers upon this world from its beginning have been in rehearsal for, and anticipation of, the giant leap in consciousness known as the golden age. This time it will not fail to be enacted in its wholeness, for so it is written.

We have yet a great hope she and I, but we dare not speak of that!

Many of the noble and great ones who sat with us in the council, the great assembly preparatory to the creation of the system to which this planet belongs, are now here either physically or in some other way moving upon the surface and within the rings of this earth. We say to you who are reading this record, if you feel deep stirrings within you as you read and ponder, you are one of us.

We encourage you to let your light shine. Do that which you most desire to do. Cease to spend days and nights in riotous living and constant seeking after pleasure that never fulfills. Give your time to study, meditation, good works. If you have the desire, you are called and have that programming.

As you begin to step into the darkness and let your light shine, you will attract to yourself, like magic, others who have similar programming for tasks and missions to perform in the preparatory work. As you contact others with similar desires, you will activate and enhance the flow of programming within each other.

Follow that which you most love. Always be open to a greater love to play upon your heartstring as you unfold. Find and be yourself. But most of all, be gentle with each other. The destruction will take care of itself. . .

Chapter Five

"He brought light out of darkness, not out of a lesser light; he can bring thy summer out of winter, though thou have no spring; though in the ways of fortune or understanding or conscience, thou have been benighted till now, wintered and frozen, clouded and eclipsed, damped and benumbed, smothered and stupified till now, now God comes to thee, not as in the dawning of the day, not as in the bud of the spring, but as the sun at noon." John Donne, 1573-1631

"For thou, Lord, art high above all the earth; thou are exalted far above all gods." Psalm 97:9

"For the Lord your God is God of gods, and lord of lords." Deuteronomy 10:17

When I left the dolphins of Mu, I promised them I would return. I told them that from the stars I would watch for the communication systems that were used on Atlantis. At such a time, when the brothers of the shadow were becoming exceedingly strong, I knew that Kira and I would touch again and be called back to earth to assist with the birth of a new age.

On our arrival, we found that the descendents of the original dolphins had retained much of the programming in their memory banks. But it was disconcerting to hear them sing for their god Marlan to come and to play with them in the form of another dolphin. They had judged the human race to be inferior because the people were asleep and easily manipulated to the dolphins' desires. It was logical for them to conclude that their ancient god Marlan either was a dolphin himself, or would take upon himself the form of a dolphin on his return.

There is still confusion among the dolphins and the people who work closely with that ring. We do not wish to diminish the service, the intellect, and the gentleness of the noble dolphin. There is much that they can teach man. But they are not men! We wish to avoid the mistakes made prior to Atlantis, when men copulated with animals. Some of the Atlantean temples sheltered rings who worked to overcome the results of those sad mismatches.

Considerable research has been done on the intelligence and communication capabilities of the dolphins since Kira and I have touched earth again. Many humans have been programmed to move within the rings of power associated with the dolphin project.

21

Those of you who are actively seeking altered states of consciousness through the use of helps such as drugs and chemicals, we suggest to you that such aids are really not necessary. There are many walking this earth who have experienced everything you have, and more, without ever having used superficial helps.

We will show you techniques that may work for you. The human mind itself is what is being explored, not some unnatural double. Man has all he needs built into himself in a natural way to explore space and time. Those who return from such pristine experiences can bear a more powerful witness because they know for sure that they have not been experiencing a flashback, or some other questionable state produced by an external mind-altering aid.

The scriptures and ancient books are filled with stories of men who have reached high levels of awareness without the use of aids other than their own brothers who work beyond the veil of mortality. When the heavens open in broad daylight and people in bright clothing descend, call you by name, talk to you, identify themselves with historic personalities, leave you with concrete objects for a specific uplifting purpose, appear again on other occasions, and are seen by several others at the same time; then you have had an experience indeed!

It is not the individual experience that counts so much as the quality of the influence that individual can have upon others.

Some wonderful energies are now moving upon this earth. They comprehend a magnificent psychology that stretches through many levels from the elemental up. We will talk more about the importance of the man and the woman melded as one eternal dyad. . .

Chapter Six

"But ye are a chosen generation, a royal priesthood, an holy nation, a peculiar people." 1 Peter 2:9

"Among the gods there is none like unto thee, O Lord; neither are there any works like unto thy works." Psalm 86:8

It was the runaway technological explosion on Atlantis that was responsible for the destruction of our beloved Mu. Not that it is incorrect to explore the shadows; the shadows also are of the gods. However, a balance must be maintained.

In every age, men are called to the priesthood rings and charged with the responsibility of working out a balance. Their powers on the physical level are limited however, to the value people place on their teachings.

In every age there are also those who usurp the powers of the priesthoods; those who seek to purchase with money that which can only be had from the gods. Thus there arise secret shadow combinations of intelligences schooled in sorcery and witchcraft. They wield amazing power among a sleeping people.

Secret combinations were very strong toward the end of Atlantis. These came about after the flying machines defiled the center and established physical contact and direct trade among the people of both continents. Crystal powers were developed to control and manipulate the people. Such forces are evident upon the earth today, to those who are trained to recognize their operations.

Some people associated with the dolphin project are actively using Atlantean crystal technology. They desire to compel lifeforms to conform to what they with their limited vision think is the only workable plan to adapt new age energies for the benefit of all mankind.

The true masters of light use only gentle persuasion, and are exceedingly careful to ensure that people have their freedom of choice.

At the center there is a plan whereby both wings can obtain balance, if they choose. Every single entity can have everything he or she desires. Sometimes however, this requires the creation of new lesser worlds. Perhaps an acceptable plan may be to reveal all the secrets of all powers moving within the levels of choice, and let the people awake and decide for themselves.

Those of you who are consciously working with the crystal powers: the iris, medical implants, food, psychology, the mobile and large mastermind groups; why is it that sometimes your powers do not work?

Could it be that occasionally a higher power you are not aware of steps in? Perhaps we have been trying to awaken you to the acknowledgement that a God comprehends all things, and is more powerful than a mastermind of the combined population of an entire star system could ever be. You kick against the pricks with your little powers, your little games that seem to you to be so comprehensive. The true order of the universe is love, gentle persuasion; and always, a greater god!

Chapter Seven

(I was on the airplane Marlan talks about. We flew from Vancouver to Calgary. I actually felt the floor shake when Kira purposely strode across the terminal. She is truly breathtaking in any disguise! It was always an incredible experience to watch Kira move. . .)

"And the likeness of the firmament upon the heads of the living creature was as the color of the terrible crystal." Ezekiel 1:22

Kira and I in a little moment of our wrath have sometimes put on our jackboots, so to speak, and gone out in power to directly confront the crystal wielders. Believe me, when Kira walks in her high heels the earth shakes! She is a master of disguise, as are all who walk with high power touching the physical level.

There is an unwritten rule that the gods as they walk among men must clean up their garbage, remove the physical evidence of their having been there, lest the people come along and be awakened prematurely out of their sleep and that god must then carry those people, perhaps for generations.

Those who work the shadow know instantly when a high power has touched down in their city, even though they may not understand the extent of the high power's programming and experience. The local metaphysical community senses only *"something else, something big"* about that person.

Recently I took a trip on an airplane. I deployed techniques to confuse and test the dark side who always follow and challenge us here and among the stars. Airline seats are booked and assigned by computers. Computers are delightful machines. They can be blamed for anything, yet they never lie!

It is easy for an advanced intelligence to cause people to sleep for the fraction of a second needed to manipulate a keyboard operator. Indeed, if you have ever blinked your eyes it is possible that in that blink an external intelligence has used your body for some purpose.

The dark side is very skillful. They tracked us and had their people aboard our flight. Kira and I were required to demonstrate our power. We did this by doing nothing at all! Such is the power that surrounds the higher masters. Powers that normally work for lower forces are rendered useless by the presence of a higher master, even if in disguise.

We can hear crystals as they are deployed in a mobile battle group, or the larger ones operating from hill to hill in power spots. We can feel their powerful rays as if they were streams of high voltage electricity moving without conductors. They do us no harm, only witness their presence and intensity, and give away their source coordinates.

High masters transcend such powers with the principle of total defenselessness. I say to you who are consciously directing the crystals; we wish you all the best as our brothers, but encourage you when your power fails to look around and consider why it has failed you.

Could the poorly dressed man, or the lovely young lady with the fascinating eyes sitting a seat or two ahead of you be a true *"Jedi Knight"*? Could the child across the aisle drawing a picture of a spaceship, and looking strangely at the man and the lovely young lady, have something to teach you?

Listen to the children. It is very difficult to hide from, or to deceive a child. Children will speak truth with the voice of adults if you will allow it. Often the masters have on their best disguise but have to move away quickly, embarrassed that a child has seen through it and is seeking validation from mother by asking highly revealing questions.

Children often detect the heartsong of a master and go to him or her in a crowd as though the master was familiar and well loved. At such a moment a golden burst of celestial light flashes though the darkness of space, to be seen among the stars. . .

The child's eyes may not be seeing an ordinary man at all, but may be scanning a powerful radiant being with eyes of fire, wearing a brown earth color or a navy blue battle jacket, with epaulets on his shoulders and the mark and flash of a young god and a king upon his countenance.

Observe the children closely if you would understand what is taking place around you at higher vibrations. Children play the games the gods play to become themselves.

Chapter Eight

"He was caught up into paradise and heard unspeakable words, which it is not lawful for a man to utter." 2 Corinthians 12:4

We are aware as I write this record that it is not organized into the usual textbook style where each chapter extensively develops or exhausts a particular topic, and where some linear progression seems to present itself. If a progression becomes evident herein it may be that the content becomes deeper and deeper from the front to the back.

If this is so, it is acceptable. As you ponder these matters it becomes easier and easier to scan more and more associations. The brain becomes exercised and trancelike learning states are achieved as limitations scale off.

We are aware that a god in the flesh is subject to the weakness of elemental matter. Communication is maimed and clumsy. My style may be peculiar and sentence structure archaic. If so that may also be a compliment to the flexibility and tolerance of the publisher of this work. I make no claim to be a famous writer disguised as a human being! We are not interested in plot, but in theme. We would teach, not entertain.

Our hope is that each paragraph will include enough associations for most experienced readers to ponder upon for some time.

We are cautious in how much we directly reveal. The prophets have always encountered things that it was not lawful for them to write, or which no written language could describe. Our design is to heat the mind to intense thinking, and to meditative trancelike pondering so synergy can be approached where one plus one equals three, the sum of the parts becomes a greater and previously unimagined whole.

The more you read the more you think, the more you think the more you ponder, the more you ponder the easier it gets to read, to think, to ponder. Learning accelerates through the use of circular equations. All power moves in circles. We leave the meaning and the application of that to your own good mind to stew upon!

Never underestimate the power of your imagination to reveal to you that which you most desire. Movies, plays, television, radio, all media, even commercials are for a specific purpose beyond their level one significance. All are powerful programming devices. Everything has different and even contradictory meanings as you evaluate the stimulus from different levels, different points of view.

You may see someone changing a flat tire along a busy street. That is a level one evaluation. If you look upon the same scene with higher faculties of awareness, you might see important contacts and relationships being established with the people who *"just happen"* to be passing by in that same space at that same time.

Nothing happens by accident. Everything has a purpose.

You might see a magnificent drama unfolding in the simple movements, the body language the person changing the tire is making. You might see how the passersby are actually moving and dancing in fluid delicate rhythm and harmony with the advanced intelligence who appears to be simply changing a tire.

You might even become aware that new worlds are being organized. People whose awareness is fixed at level one are seeing only an unfortunate person working tediously, but carefully, on an old blue automobile. . .

Chapter Nine

"For, behold, the Lord will come with fire, and with his chariots like a whirlwind to render his anger with fury, and his rebuke with flames of fire. For by fire and by his sword will the Lord plead with all flesh; and the slain of the Lord shall be many." Isaiah 66:15,16

"And they shall go forth, and look upon the carcases of the men that have transgressed against me: for their worm shall not die, neither shall their fire be quenched. . ." Isaiah 66:24

"For the Lord hath poured out upon you the spirit of deep sleep, and hath closed your eyes. . ." Isaiah 29:10

Often in the past, to speak of even level two meanings to a level one awareness was to risk being labelled insane, strange, peculiar. Science and art are now converging upon the mountaintops. Higher level meanings are understood and wondered upon in closed circles meeting in safe places, to discuss the undiscussable.

The secrets of the gods used to be closely held for a few initiates only. New age energies open all secrets to all people. All doors are open now. You need only dare to walk through. When you have found safety in your own inner being, you are prepared to let go of external objects that establish identity in spacetime. You can then safely move beyond sight of the shore; as you must if you would discover new lands.

A little child holds tight to the matrix; then moves away a bit, explores and makes its surroundings familiar, thus safe. Even then the child scurries back for a quick hug and reassurance that mother is there and the universe is unfolding as it should.

Once you have discovered your inner essence and established it as your matrix, you can safely venture anywhere, anytime, and still be home. Home is where you are. Stilling the mind may be a correct beginning technique for you, to establish your matrix.

All creativity, imagination, is simply reawakening former memories. The philosophy of education based upon the child being a *"tabula rasa"*, an empty slate upon which the teacher is to write; or an empty vase waiting to be filled by the wisdom of the teacher's flowery prose; needs to be examined more carefully for its reverse possibilities. If you are able to imagine something, you have already created it at a higher level. It is patterned after something you have known from some other space, some other time.

29

The concept of space and time is only an illusion for a specific purpose in the master plan. Creative people who encounter the muse: authors, actors, artists, often become consciously aware of this.

The *"Jedi Knights"*, the close encounters, the Adama's and their voyages among the stars in search of planet earth; all these things are founded in reality at higher levels. Each quality movie, each story that stirs the heart and the imagination, each uplifting sound of music, each *"Somewhere in Time"* is a powerful psychology teaching the people that such things are possible, instilling in the people the faith to make the suddenly believable, the desirable, become the real.

You are constantly being programmed for expansion of awareness, and for the evolution of new physical manifestations designed for your progress and learning. You receive line upon line, precept upon precept, here a little and there a little, that you may learn to walk properly before we ask you to run, then to fly. You are fed milk before strong meat. We do not suddenly reach out, grab your hand unawares and jump off a cliff. We do not push you out of the nest prematurely. But we may give a gentle nudge!

Neither do we say that the master will not come suddenly to his temple; nor that none will be destroyed by the fire of his coming. Be prepared in all things. There is a voice of warning abroad throughout the land. Hasten, hasten your preparations.

You are kept half asleep until you are psychologically prepared to be thrust awake and aware into a brand new world and confrontation with strange forces and beings you thought existed only in the media, in dreams, and in nightmares. The gods are gentle. They have been where you are!

It is said that a master is one who has started out a bit sooner than the student. Perhaps it is you yourself operating at levels of which you choose to remain unaware who controls your own progress, your own destiny, your own journey back to the center where others wait to welcome you home.

Perhaps the gods and the hierarchy simply coordinate movements, enforce rules, maintain balance, send love, reach out helping hands, allow freedom to choose, assist the Gods. Could you yourself already be a master to lower worlds when your body sleeps on earth?

Technology hastens the speed at which the gods may prepare a people for their awakening. In pretechnological ages should a god choose to speak, on level one the message might be heard in its pure form by only a handful of scattered initiates and loosely linked priesthood rings and prophets. Others might hear only thunder in the sky when there are no clouds, a wind when there is no breeze, the sound of rushing water upon the stillness of a desert day, or nothing at all.

With technology, a god may inspire a drama, a program that all can see with physical eyes and ears wide open and aware.

The priesthood who work awake and aware in physical form can now bounce their message to millions from a central place, through microwave and satellite links. The work preparatory to the golden age must be done perfectly; but it must also be hastened. The awakening of a people and the splitting of a world is a great and a terrible time. The bubble of perceived reality and psychological stability must be stretched almost to bursting.

We choose not to write much about the programming techniques of secret combinations on both wings. Although we know a balance must be kept and a master plan is in operation, in the darkness of this world Kira and I are in our wrath when we see how devious are the ways of man.

Such things are revealed to many and will yet be shouted from the housetops for all to know and to choose for themselves which to accept, and which to reject. Perhaps people will choose to have nothing to do with any!

A greater God is in the heavens. The timing is perfect; all is known. Should one ring or essential link choose not to play, another is prepared with dual programming to take its place. Many are foreordained to specific tasks long before they reach mortality. . .

Chapter Ten

"For we wrestle not against flesh and blood, but against principalities, against powers, and against the rulers of the darkness of this world. . ."
Ephesians 6:12

"If thine enemy hunger, feed him; for in so doing thou shalt heap coals of fire on his head." Romans 12:20

The Orwellian world of 1984 is at your doors in such a way as you have never imagined possible. Powers, principalities, thrones, dominions struggle desperately for the hearts and minds of the people. The worth and cost of a human soul is known, and it is priceless.

The physical world is illusion. Powers move and manipulate your minds and bodies at will unless you are awake and aware to their operations.

As I write this, I am stirred to anger and feel I should put on my jackboots and go out flashing fire from my eyes as we once did with our technology. Yet I am restrained, it is not the present way nor the hour. The warrior-king lives yet in the heart of Marlan. Perhaps there is a purpose for that, somewhere in time!

Powerful techniques known in their basic form by such concepts as *"biofeedback"* and *"behavior modification"*, are used to program people for specific movements. These methods are applied during the trancelike states invoked by giving attention to the media. A commentator recently put it quite succinctly, stating: *"The medium is the message".*

Red lights on smoke detectors and electronic devices can be used to hasten accelerated programming by giving a subliminal suggestion to put out the light with the imagination or willpower. *(The ubiquitous red crystals could even resemble the all-seeing eye of Orwell's "Big Brother").*

As you watch video screens and listen to audio devices, static and unpleasant barely discernable high or low frequency sounds can be used to condition you when certain key emotions or messages are being presented to the conscious mind. Your emotions, and therefore most of the belief systems that motivate your behavior patterns, can be played with and associated with the real message of indoctrination that is being delivered.

Your mind is capable of reading microdots flashed upon the screen, unseen by level one awareness. Later you will do things for reasons

32

you do not know. Through television, thousands of people can be conditioned to the same response upon presentation of a cue known only to the master programmers.

Should you raise a clamor regarding such a possibility, you may be labelled *"paranoid"* and locked up in a hospital or asylum to be tortured into submission to consensus reality with chemicals, psychology, and electric shocks. The doctors believe they are earning a legitimate income. They are relying on their textbooks, colleagues, and training for validity.

We are only skimming the surface of a powerful psychology that can easily be wielded by secret combinations. Such technologies may be necessary to hasten the work of expanding consciousness through accelerated learning. However, like wildfire they need to be carefully supervised by someone, somewhere. Who would you trust with total control over your mind and body?

On the positive side, you may become so absorbed in a television program that external spacetime ceases to exist for you. You are operated upon for your learning and are drawn into the program. You find that you can communicate with people on the screen. They seem to see you as you see them. You nod your head slightly and someone looks directly at you, smiles and nods back. You think a thought or a question and someone on the screen turns and responds. Your faith becomes knowledge. You are ready for accelerated learning.

Others in another room watching the same program are living their own dream, creating their own personalities and interactions.

You learn that every movement of the human body is language, a sign to those in secret combinations. You discover that others read your mind at certain levels completely. You are totally predictable and controlled by your habits and past conditioning. The eyes of your understanding are open to the operations of power within the levels of choice. You come to know that which you had never before considered. You come to know that you have never before thought for yourself. Your whole life has been controlled and manipulated by external forces.

Presidents, prime ministers, kings, queens, emperors, have been controlled in the same manner. Which wields more power, the blind puppet sitting on a throne, or the unseen magician who dangles the strings from a hidden cabinet?

Should you become awake and aware to these things and desire to minimize their influence upon your personal consciousness, a key technique may be to become flexible in your movements upon the physical plane.

Deliberately change your habits for a while. Think for yourself. Ask yourself before you do something, *"Why will I do this?"* Before

33

you go somewhere ask yourself, *"Do I really want to go?"* If you don't want to go, why go? Answer such questions after careful consideration of your motives and the choices available. You are beginning to evaluate your past and to program yourself.

Change the colors of your wardrobe. Tie your shoelaces a different way. Rearrange your furniture. Throw out the garbage. Sort through your possessions. Keep only that which you truly desire. Make last instant changes in plans and movements. Watch a different video series. Read a different sort of book. Do these things just for a little while, lest they become an obsession.

Changes in behavior patterns will cause confusion, frustration, and the lessening of your usefulness to external rings who have hitherto used you because they could predict your behavior precisely, and thus control and manipulate you through lower level communication.

Above all, replace fear with love. The emotion called love has a higher order of vibration than fear, and thus can shield you from lower level manipulations. A useful technique is to accept fears by sending them a thought of love, and the message *"welcome to our system!"*

Everything is first spiritually or mentally created. Nothing happens on the physical level until it has already happened on a higher level. You are powerless to manipulate even a joint of your body without first a mental message to do so being translated into physical equivalence, then flashed to the operant systems.

Thus an intelligence attuned to higher levels can predict movement on the physical level long before it happens. In that way a master is never in danger. He is attuned to everything around him and operates his body in a space and time that a lower intelligence cannot penetrate. The lesser intelligence may not even be aware of the master's presence, other than perhaps having a strange feeling that something is different, someone is near!

Chapter Eleven

"One day is with the Lord as a thousand years, and a thousand years as one day." 2 Peter 3:8

Consider the waves of the ocean as they crash into the shore. You can predict with certainty what will happen as the collision occurs. You can see the wave as it approaches, and you know what has happened before. You are centered in the same spacetime as those movements.

Consider now the plankton, the seaweed, the dead and the living entities that move within the waters. Consider the similarity of the mountains to the waves; the forests, flowers, and animals to the plankton, as they live and move upon the mountains.

Could it be that a god standing in a different spacetime than yours could see the mountains flowing like the waves of the sea? Could that god predict the future of that landform and the creatures who live thereon?   Could it be that a thousand years upon the earth may be but a day on the center of a system? Could it be that when you blink an eyelid a higher intelligence might have an hour to manipulate and move upon your body? Ponder upon space, time, and your own identity. . .

Every single thing manifest on the physical plane is there for your learning. Higher levels of your mind even now may be recording something that is happening upon some distant galaxy, that may one day be important to your development or responsibility.

You are conscious in the moment only of that which you are paying attention to. As you advance in awareness you are beginning to pay attention to more and more stimuli at the same time, and are learning to use sensory faculties you have not even dreamed of before.

As you become aware of something, as your attention is being drawn to a pattern of stimuli, regardless of which sensory organs are being used, ask yourself, *"Why have I created this?" "What do I have to learn from this?"*

As you become aware of something, you yourself have created that awareness. Others may not see or hear what you are aware of and therefore to them it does not exist. If you are aware of it, it is your own creation.

You always act in your own best interests. Your best interests are to learn that which you were not previously aware of. Make asking yourself those two questions a habit, just for a little time. In an amazingly short while the world will begin to turn for you. Everything will become a sign, a clue, a teaching/learning situation for your benefit.

You ponder something and suddenly become aware that the people passing by are talking about that very thing. Listen to what the people are saying. They are asleep to themselves; they know not what they are doing. You are controlling them. They are talking for your learning.

As you ponder further you observe that the radio, the television, the newspapers, are all focussed on what you are thinking. The memory of old commercials and jingles comes to mind with powerful associations that further develop your learning on the subject. Soon even the theaters are showing movies for you. You may discover that you have lived the last sixteen years with an American actor and the *"Hebrew Oilers"* pouring oil into people's lamps, that they may be ready for the coming of the bridegroom. Your mastership has not come naturally by accident!

Observe your surroundings carefully, especially the people. You will observe how someone walking near you suddenly changes in appearance or behavior as you or an external magic ring now bound to serve your mastery moves upon that person to convey information to you, or perhaps to protect you from other entities that are displaced by a now higher master. You are beginning to control the lesser spirits by consciously doing nothing, nothing at all!

Chapter Twelve

As Kira and I move in the physical world, we are offered gifts, new identities, vehicles, tickets. I turn them all down. We have sufficient for our needs and refrain from operating in magic except as we choose to become aware of magical movements about us. I maintain an unbroken stream of consciousness as I move with physical form.

The concept of *"walk-ins"* offers an acceptable psychology to explain certain phenomena that are not understood on this earth. Perhaps this is because people fail to comprehend the vast faculties of the human mind which at the same instant can touch earth, and span the heavens to contact God.

It is awareness, the limiting of one's attention, that leads the carnal human mind to question its own exalted status. People are literally the offspring of a greater God who directs all life within galaxies without number, and who offers each offspring an inheritance of everything that exists. Thus it is known that the worth of a single human soul is beyond price. . .

And yet, isn't romance fun. . .!

Wouldn't it be fun to be a God and to populate your own worlds with all diversities of people and lifeforms; each human learning to be a god as you had learned on other worlds?

Wouldn't it be fun to walk among them in disguise; to *"walk-in"* to the body of Antony or Cleopatra, or both at the same time! To share their moments of exquisite delight; their heights of passion, joy, sorrow. Perhaps without you they wouldn't have such a complete span of emotion.

As God you would transcend all mortal rules and laws. You have already worked through their purpose. You could experience the entire spectrum of human emotion without being ensnared and bound to any. You could have anything and everything you desire.

You could walk among your people as a healer; experiencing and sharing their love, their peaks of joy, awe, gratitude, as they feel miracles flow from your fingertips, see mountains move by the majesty of your coming.

You could be Jesse James, Patton, Moses, Noah, Brigham Young with his many wives, a great composer, an artist of renown, a Mother Teresa, Anastasia, a beautiful queen, a nightingale, a little child learning to reflect her mother's smile.

You could share the loneliness of Adam, Michael, the Ancient of Days alone in the garden; and the fulness of their joy when you called to him his lovely bride from the stars.

You could walk in a land where infants die in their mother's arms when the milk dries, and flies crawl unheeded over parched unfeeling lips. You would feel their pain, sorrow, helplessness. You could wash their feet with your tears as you pass by unknown, your begging bowl clutched to an emaciated breast.

The next moment you would smile and take joy with them as they pass from mortality and see you as an angel of light. You show them that the bodies left behind are illusion; only vehicles for their greater learning. You chuckle together as they comprehend how seriously they have taken the jest the gods had played upon the earth.

You could pause at a camp of Gypsies in the night, dance once around their camp fire, and create a legend that would be told to babes for hundreds of years; share the wild rapture of a coven of witches flying naked and free on the beams of a full moon; dance with the little people, laugh with the gnomes and the elves; be a river, a lake, a warm sea, the womb of countless lifeforms. You could live all books, all movies, all characters, all history, all futures. . .

But most of all, as you walk as God among your people, you would recognize your Kira or Marlan in any disguise. You could chase each other laughing through worlds, galaxies, systems. And when you touch, you would make love as only the Gods know how. Galaxies would move for you, a new universe explode into being. It is You for whom the bell tolls, the songs are sung, the stories are written, the dramas are played. . .

Such is the purpose of man, that all may be trained as gods; that all may have a fulness of joy and experience. It is exquisite to have a complete relationship with the Gods!

Chapter Thirteen

"And thou shalt take no gift; for the gift blindeth the wise, and perverteth the words of the righteous." Exodus 23:8

Should I be in a restaurant in a strange city where the rings are not accustomed to me and I telephone for a taxi, soon a white car will pull up, the keys will be left in the ignition, the driver will move out of sight, and I know it is there by the operations of a white master of the seventh level. Since I never take such a vehicle, soon someone else in the restaurant will look at me with surprise and delight and will move off with the car themselves. The people sleep and notice nothing unusual. Such is the operation of rings of power and secret combinations which recognize about me a masterflash that indicates to them they must obey and fulfill my mental desires.

I am aware that in refusing to accept the gifts offered to me, I am deliberately creating confusion and anxiety as entities who are trained to obedience suddenly encounter an unpredictable master. Yet maybe in this they may learn to think for themselves.

Perhaps it is time for everything to change now. Maybe even the demons should no longer be cast out by force, but be encouraged by love and gentle persuasion to follow the master to green pastures where still waters flow and the soul can find peace from its torment, and a teacher to bathe their fevered brow with the coolness of living waters; to cleanse forever from their tongues the foul stench of hatred and misunderstanding.

All lifeforms need love. All need hugs. Be gentle with each other. Let enmity cease from the land that earth too may rest for a season. Perhaps this time, after another forty years in the wilderness, Moses will be allowed to enter the promised land together with the people.

Consider these things, and govern your actions accordingly. . .

Should I take a bus for a lengthy trip, especially if through the night, I no sooner board the bus than I am surrounded by an escort of young men who look and talk like soldiers. As we move outside the city into the night I observe that the driver is being controlled by one of the mobile combat group. Another soldier is in a trancelike state searching for coordinates and listening for my mental desires. Should I stand up, immediately one ahead and one behind will stand as I stand, move as I move, and turn as I turn.

They never seem to understand that I am serious in taking the bus all the way to my destination. They grumble among themselves after a few miles and search for coordinates to the starship they assume I am merely covering my tracks to in taking an earthbound bus from the city.

Should I talk to them and send love, they will appear at first shocked, then delighted. Gradually they find I am a gentle master and do not hold them to their task. Soon after, several will leave and go their separate ways. None anymore follows me slavishly.

There are differences in the quality of combat escorts, according to the space we traverse on a planet, and the type of forces which claim that space as their own.

Often on a night trip the little people come on board and travel a few miles before the bus stops to let them off somewhere in the dark. They come to see and to test this strange intelligence that crosses their space. Usually one will touch me physically to ensure I am real on level one. I see them as young women, perhaps four to five feet tall. They are delightful to watch as they stand in a circle of three, bend their heads together, and chuckle with secrets and tales; enjoying the companionship of the night. . .

Chapter Fourteen

"When the light is made to move in a circle, all the energies of heaven and earth, of the light and dark, are crystallized. That is what is termed seed-like thinking, or purification of the energy, or purification of the idea. When one begins to apply this magic it is as if, in the middle of being, there were non-being." Lu Yen, A.D. 800

"Force never moves in a straight line, but always in a curve vast as the universe, and therefore eventually returns whence it issued forth, but upon a higher arc for the universe has progressed since it started." Kabbalah

Hierarchies of power operate throughout the universe. For example, let us say there are seven operational levels, bodies, states of awareness.

A master of physical level one operations will have earned a belt like a martial arts belt; in this case a red one. He will generate a red flash of light that will be seen by intelligences operating below the level of mastership on level one. A level two master will flash yellow and has mastered astral/emotional operations. A level three master has mastered mental operations and will flash perhaps orange to those below.

A level three master will often be a sorcerer or witch and will direct a ring of magic in which there may be other witches, shamans, psychics, who may not be consciously aware of their own power and position in the ring, except perhaps in dreams, out of body experiences, and during intense mental effort to control and manipulate others. They will be aware of many *"coincidences"* occurring in their life, and of strange patterns of manifestation about them.

Each of these operations include intelligences who are not physically manifest to people whose awareness is limited to level one. The lower three levels are the dark worlds of illusion and choice. Freedom of choice operates within these levels by universal decree. The masters are careful to ensure that each individual has his or her free agency, except as it is limited by others operating with awareness only in the choice levels.

Masters who operate above level three have already chosen to obey the mind and will of god. That part of their consciousness is trained to obedience. A level five master is a god to a level four master who will recognize a certain flash about the level five intelligence. If the two are moving on the same arc and ring of stewardship, the level four master will hear the voice of the level five master as the voice of god.

For each master there are many apprentices. Any master may

command operations on all lower levels simply by speaking. His voice will be heard and obeyed as the voice of god.

These illustrations are simply descriptive of learning/teaching situations when viewed above level three. It has been written that all the world is a stage. It may be that all the universe is a stage as well; a stage designed for the gods to play the game of becoming God.

Perhaps we may all awaken one day upon a celestial world filled with the most beautiful people imaginable, and find that God has been showing us a television clip that we became absorbed in for a few moments. . .

As you read this, I suggest however that you not attempt to hold your breath while you await such an awakening!

Chapter Fifteen

"The wheels of time are mysterious. Time is a concept of mind. Without mind, there is no concept of time. Annihilate the mind. You will go beyond time. You will enter the realm of Timeless. You will live in the Eternal." Sivananda

"I heard also the noise of the wheels over against them, and a voice of a great rushing." Ezekiel 3:13

At certain levels of preparation in the training of a young god, he passes through the most terrifying and fearful experience the Gods could create. This occurs only after enormous preparation, choices, and training. He is not aware what the preparation is leading up to. His mind has been trained to span galaxies, his logic has never failed, he knows all things. . .

The young confident god with fire in his glance and worlds at his fingertips suddenly becomes aware that he is strapped powerless to a wheel that is spinning at a very high rate of speed. The mind that has never failed is presented with an impossible problem. Like a monstrous computer with an impossible problem it works through every possible combination, spinning faster and faster and faster. . .

And it is *YOU!*

You live your whole life, and lives and eons of time again in a moment, and every single movement you have ever made and every single thought you ever had and every sound you ever heard, and you are moving faster, and faster, and faster, and getting dizzier and dizzier and dizzier, and you are powerless to burn yourself out, and you try and you can't and you live the entire history of the world; you live the bible, all books, movies, stories, tales, you live the experiences of all the masters and teachers, children, mothers, wives, and you search desperately; and you are being *CRUCIFIED* on a wheel that spins faster and faster and faster. . .

You examine every particle of dust, every microbe upon the whole planet, searching for a clue. You know that if you don't solve the problem the whole universe will crash in on everyone, and gods and Gods, and billions and billions of people, families and children are counting on you, you, *YOU* alone can do it and no else can. . .and you can't find the clue, and you know the problem is impossible to solve, and you know you can't handle this and you know you can't get off the wheel and you know that the only way off the wheel. . .is to put someone else on it. . .And you love that someone else more than anything. Nothing else matters. . .

You can't do it, but you can't stop the wheel, and the problem is impossible to solve. . .

You become evil, and good, and good and evil, and evil and good, and the only way off is to put someone else on the wheel, and it goes round and it goes round and it goes round, and round and round; and no you can't, and no you won't, you can't you won't, you can't do it, you must do it, and it's impossible. . . but you must. . . you must. . .you must put *KIRA* on the wheel!

Then, and only then do you know that Kira put you there. . .

And if you put Kira on the wheel she'll put you there, and if she puts you there, you'll put her there, and it goes round and it goes round and it goes round, and at last, at last when you finally disintegrate completely; when the last particle that was ever you spins off beyond the last galaxy, the last system, the last universe; when you are nothing, nothing, nothing at all. . .then you begin to comprehend what it is to be a god!

Then, and only then do you just begin to comprehend in a tiny, tiny way what it is to sweat blood from every pore. . .to sweat blood as another did for us. . .in Gethsemane!

Chapter Sixteen

"When thy reason has crossed the entanglements of illusion, then shalt thou become indifferent both to the philosophies thou has heard and to those thou mayest yet hear." Bhagavad Gita, B.C. 400

On Mu the dolphins would come inside my mountain retreat through underground passages that connected with the sea. My thoughts were their coordinates.

The airships of Atlantis first took their coordinates and navigated by the system of underground streams, the planet's veins and capillaries, that are found criss-crossed throughout the earth. These coordinates were mapped by the ancients. Dowsers and those who work knowledgeably with radiesthesia take their programming from these memories. Later, the Atlanteans set up their own surface systems, like the navigational aids of today, with crystal rays and streams of mastermind thought flowing silently from the temples.

In the worlds of spirit, level two in particular, there are bounds set to the space in which certain types of intelligence may travel. Those who have experienced vivid dreams and out of the body travel could well have been navigating subconsciously by the old coordinates that are yet impressed upon their mind, even as the dolphins retain their ancient programming after many generations.

Navigation becomes confusing as man develops technology and erects unnatural systems of electrical and high frequency transmission. The astral body is attracted to these transmissions; the high voltage towers, telephone lines, microwaves, radio beacons, underground cables, pipelines. Each becomes an influencing factor to enter into the navigation computers, lest you miss your coordinates and become lost, or stray beyond your set boundaries into a territory ruled by a more powerful force than yours.

Some of you may have witnessed the phenomena of ball lightning, a light or fire, a *"UFO"* that appears to follow electrical lines or any other man-made straight line. Each time a new man made structure is erected it must be mapped and entered into the ancient systems.

Such a structure may facilitate locomotion for some types of vehicles that borrow from those energies, or use them as a simple navigational aid to their destination. Fluctuations and failures in electrical power grids may be due on occasion to influences which are beyond the knowledge and calculations of their designers and operators.

Electrical power engineers sometimes view the giant grids as a temperamental *"black cat"* that could pounce on its maker at any moment.

Consider how much your lives, cities, identity, are dependent upon an orderly flow of a little-understood, petulant, invisible force. What would you do if the poles reversed, if even batteries suddenly ceased to function?

Who would you become. . .?

Chapter Seventeen

"And I will shew wonders in the heavens and in the earth, blood, and fire, and pillars of smoke. The sun shall be turned into darkness, and the moon into blood, before the great and terrible day of the Lord come."
Joel 2:30,31

As I travel through a city I can choose to become aware of the forces moving about me. I can observe the shadow side who track and search for me here and among the stars. I notice as they come alongside in another car that they scan an arc a few degrees ahead or behind me. They cannot see me because their heads are not in line with mine, their coordinates are altered by the powers that move about me.

You may experience this yourself in symbolic form. Listen for a high frequency hum from a source such as a light bulb controlled by a dimmer switch. Turn your head slowly when you have located the hum. You will become aware that the sound is found only in thin sheets. This is similar to the sounds we hear from the crystals and the dolphins.

Sometimes another lifeform, one of the people who sleep, will be moved in the direction the shadow side is searching. This will temporarily distract them. It is recorded that Jesus could move unseen out of hostile crowds. Perhaps he deployed similar techniques.

Another reason why the preparatory work in these days must be hastened is that pollution is altering the magnetic properties of lakes, seas, and underground streams. This causes confusion and chaos in the orderly system set up by the ancients to contain, control, and set boundaries within the spirit levels of this earth.

It is all for a purpose of course and was known beforehand. The splitting of a world is first done at the spirit level. Yet there can arise intense panic and psychological trauma among spirits who suddenly find their familiar territory no longer familiar, and thus perceived to be unsafe.

Consider too the strain upon the guards and gatekeepers as the walls of their keep tumble. No longer are doorways approached only by people knowing passwords, keys and signs. . .

The prison doors are open, asylums abandoned, hospitals emptied, cities left desolate as the chaos of sudden change bursts the bubble of consensus reality. People flee to their own. Families, tribes, groups move about the land searching for and demanding sustenance from others. No longer do the trucks roll, no longer are the market shelves restocked while the people sleep.

Only the saints, those who have been touched on the one hand; those with their own matrix, those with a song on their lips and love in their hearts; those who hope, those who heed the signs of the times, are safely gathered into refuges from the storm, the whirlwinds, the flames, the earthquakes, the blood that cleanses the land and sweeps off all who have chosen not to change, and who are consigned therefore to another lesser world for generations more of search, struggle, and fearful clumsy learning.

How great for some, and how terrible for others are these the last days of a planet who has fulfilled her relationships, and is about to shuck off her rings of pollution, and to rise again to her paradise state.

Chapter Eighteen

"And Moses said unto God, Behold when I come unto the children of Israel, and shall say unto them, The God of your fathers hath sent me unto you; and they shall say to me, What is his name? what shall I say unto them? And God said unto Moses, I AM THAT I AM: and he said, Thus shalt thou say unto the children of Israel, I AM hath sent me unto you." Exodus 3:13,14

"My soul, what's lighter than a feather? Wind. Than wind? The fire. And what than fire? The Mind. What's lighter than the mind? A thought. Than thought? This bubble world. What than this bubble? Nought." Quarles, 1592-1644

"Let us be silent, that we may hear the whispers of the gods." Emerson, 1803-1882

Who are you? Where do you stand when your identity is completely stripped from you on the wheel, the rack of a greater god, intent on making you as he and she are?

You have been shopping in a strange city, adrift in a foreign land, lost in the woods, castaway on a sea, panicked by the thickness of the fog, thrust suddenly into a war, defenseless in some dark alley where others lurk to take your purse and your life.

Who are you then? Do you weep for mercy? Are you dizzy and disoriented? How is it that you can become lost? What is lost?

In a shopping mall in a strange city you are alone and you lose your way. You are surrounded by people and everything money can buy, but you panic. You can't remember where you left your car. You want to get back to its safety. Your car is home. You identify your vehicle as yourself. . .

Remove the car from your mind; you need no longer return to it. Remove your family, your house. Free yourself from all former relationships. Empty your pockets; throw away your keys, your identification papers, your money.

Go out from the city. Find a private place in the mountains. Remove the shoes from your feet, the clothing from your body, the rings from your ears, the jewelry from your hand, the watch from your wrist. Drop all possessions into a swiftly moving mountain stream that carries them forever from your sight.

Wash the stains from your hands, the makeup from your face, the commercial smells from your body and nostrils. No longer does anyone

49

on earth know you. None shall come looking to find you. No one else cares.

You make a warm shelter from the trees, a bed from their boughs. There is food and water. . .

Who are you? What is left? Is it a birth or a death? Are you in prison, a hospital, an asylum?

"You shall know the truth and the truth shall make you free." Are you free?

That which you identify with controls you. That which you do not identify with, you have power to control. The car in the parking lot was yours; it drew you back. You were a family; they drew you back. You thought others would miss you; you identified yourself as another. Your possessions became your identity. They controlled you. You were lost without them. You wanted to go back to them to find yourself.

Now, in the wilderness of your becoming you have burned all the bridges behind you. Perhaps a nuclear device, an earthquake, a whirlwind, has destroyed your home city. Relatives and friends are consumed in its wrath. None can reach you. No one cares. . .

Try to remember everything you did last year, last month, last week, yesterday; all that you saw, you heard, you smelled, you tasted, you touched. Remember your childhood if you can; what you wore, how you were taught to speak, to crawl, to walk. Are even your bones the same now as when you were born? Erase the past, you have already done so. Forget your name; it is nothing when there are none to call it, none to affirm your identity, none to control you in that fashion.

You say you have memory but you don't, you have only now. You have only a relationship with that which you are presently aware of. You can't remember another face. There is no time, none to form a consensus.

Are you old or young? How can you tell? You have no comparison, no past. Are you male or female? Who is there to tell you, or why should it matter?

When you meet your death does another die as you, or are you alone without possessions? What is your identity when you have nothing, when you are nothing, not even a body? Who are you? Were you ever anything, anything at all?

Lift out of your body, away from the trees, the mountains, the earth. Close your eyes, your ears, your senses. You have nothing external to relate to, nothing to identify with.

Do you have identity without relationships? Are you alive without others, other people, other things? Do others exist without you, or another? Who are you then?

You needn't go to the mountains or give up your possessions to find the answer. You needn't die, except to your identity which never was you anyway. You may train your mind to perfect stillness. . .

50

Begin by imagining you have a hollow conduit that goes in one ear and out the other. Stand back from yourself and channel every thought you become aware of into the conduit. It goes right out the other ear. Soon you notice that every sound, every thought, every senseless jingle, every piece of song, all old conversation, is simply channeled into the conduit and you are aware only of yourself watching.

With practice the conduit leaves, it gets easier and easier. Then you learn to blank out the past, to reach outside the limits of your body and understanding. There is no memory, no external distraction, no identity, no relationship. Do you cease to exist?

Such a technique is simple, it gets easier and easier. You are exploring new time, new space, new worlds, a new frontier.

You take a voyage among the stars, or to the center where the heart dwells. You see or feel something there. You remove your shoes, walk upon holy ground. The stars take form, fall, and appear before you. You talk to another who has also been there. You find that you both have witnessed the same thing. You now have a small consensus reality, a shared identity with something formerly unknown.

When everyone becomes insane, when everyone has seen the new world, insanity ceases to exist. The new world becomes reality, the old has ceased to be fun. . .

Meanwhile, we suggest that you keep one foot upon the ground and keep your golden voyages short and sweet!

Chapter Nineteen

"And look that nothing remain in thy working mind but a naked intent stretching unto God; not clothed in any special thought of God in himself or any of his works, but only that He is as He is. . .Forsake good thoughts as well as evil thoughts. He asks no help but only thyself. He will thou do but look upon Him and let him alone." The Cloud of Unknowing, 14th Century

"Not by speech, not by mind; not by sight can He be apprehended. How can He be comprehended otherwise than by one's saying "He Is"?" Upanishads, B.C. 800

"I am the taste in the water, the light of the sun and the moon, the sound in the ether, the ability in man, the fragrance of the earth, the heat in the fire, the life of all that lives, the strength of the strong, the intelligence of the intelligent, and the original seed of all existences." Bhagavad Gita, B.C. 400

The question beyond experience remains then, does man exist without relationships?

Should you experience a moment of complete stillness, a moment when there is no past, no present, no future, no thought, no identity, no relationship; you would discover simply that you *ARE*! There can be no oblivion for man. Such is the cross he bears. That discovery is made only when you cease to think. . .

"Cogito ergo sum", I think therefore I exist or I am, is typical of thought within maya the world of illusion. Everything in maya, the levels of choice, is seen as if looking in a mirror. You see the reverse image, as if *"through a glass darkly"*. The professor of language who reads this book may now understand my peculiar sentence structure!

A good rule in all things may be to search for the opposite. There you will find truth also, and of an equal weight and balance with the other wing. *"I think therefore I am"* should be reversed should it not? *"I am, therefore I think"* could be a more correct expression, leading to a greater truth.

In perfect stillness you discover your inner essence, a state of simply *BEING*. You discover *I AM*.

The god of the Old Testament identified himself to Moses as *"I AM"*. A writer penned, *"to be or not to be, that is the question"*. Are we or are we not? Experience gives only one answer, one simple truth: Who are you? Who am I? *I AM*!

You see a statue by Rodin. You stand back, admire, take delight, joy in its perfect form, its symmetry, the beauty of its looks, the depth of its meaning. You move closer, from your purse remove a magnifying glass, examine the statue's surface, see cracks, tiny holes, crevices, shadows, faults, imperfections.

You see the clay from which it was formed. The beauty had been in your own eye, your own feelings, the sharing of the love, the uplifting thoughts, the skills, the aura, the careful labor of the artist. You shared for a moment his muse. You were where the artist was, you saw his eyes as yours, his interests as your own. . .

You look for your god in a rock, a stone, a lump of clay. You shall find him there. He is where you are, you where your awareness is centered. The beauty all along is in your own eye, your eye where your thoughts dwell, your span of depths and heights as you choose your limitations.

A prophet is not without honor except in his own city, among his own people. His own stand too close; they see the clay wherein he dwells. They see the tiny holes, the faults of the past, the shadows, the imperfections. They see him where their own identity is centered. He is where they are. He can do no miracle among them; he must be a false prophet. . .

Can anything good come out from Nazareth? Can anything good come from a tabernacle of clay, a statue that stands in the mud? Can anything of god come from a man?

If you look for my footprints upon the sand, you will find them there. . .

Much of the basic psychology behind motivation to action in maya, the world of illusion, is based upon fear. That which is not familiar, the unknown and therefore the unpredictable, is approached always with caution, if at all.

Consensus reality, identifying with fixed sensory inputs established though conditioning, forms the basic foundation for order and cooperation in developing a technological political/economic order. That which disrupts the status quo, anything that rocks the boat of state, is usually met with resistance and force by the established political power base.

Through the ages, prophets and masters have been looked upon strangely, persecuted, jailed, murdered, crucified by their own people in their own country; only to be resurrected, dusted off, given honor and applause after their death. They have dared to preach the unpreachable, a new and better way of life in defiance of the existing structure; or a return to sound basic truths that have worked for the good order, the progress and joy of mankind since time began.

It is not the common people who start the scoffing, the resistance to change, the persecution of the prophets. It is usually the lawyers, politicians, priests and ministers; the learned men, those with status and money at risk; those whose identity is founded upon fixed time and space; those who deny new revelation for their day, having twisted the former to their own purpose and limited understanding to subdue and control the masses; those who know not the god within themselves, those who are proud and arrogant in the vain imaginations of their own minds; those who have failed to establish a safe inner matrix of their own and thus dare not venture upon new uncharted waters.

The health professionals, those who profess to know more about people than do the people themselves, and who thus charge money for their services; establish their profession upon symbols, labels, a language of their own that is secret and confusing to all except the initiates who pass through their own schools and institutions of training. To explain the unexplainable they give it a label, a circular word that makes nothing clear to the understanding. They build up a psychology that creates the symptoms of disease, insanity, notwellness.

The physical body may actually be a dancing, flowing, rhythmic pattern of integrated energy. If so, all pathology becomes psychological; all therapy psychotherapy. . .

Yet I dare not expound further on this at present or risk alienation and confusion upon those who are caught up helplessly by the economics of existing systems; and upon those who would speedily destroy with their hatreds and negative attitudes that which is already dead and self-decaying.

Combine that which you feel is for you in correct relationships. Establish teaching/learning situations in which you accept another's interests as your own. In this you will do much to further the preparations that must be done for yourself, to fulfill your desire to be of service, and the effectiveness of your linking with chains that set growth patterns for thousands of others. . .

Chapter Twenty

(I witnessed many of the things described by Marlan in this chapter. I must have spent several days in an altered state of consciousness, because they all seemed so real, and so present-time. I saw the events he describes on television. Today, I rationalize them to myself as something in the future that happened as if in a dream. 1984 consensus reality fails to support what happened. Yet I saw those things clearly. Maybe I was caught in some kind of "time-warp", or as Marlan would say, "a blink of an eyelid". Or, maybe I was seeing into the spirit realms in broad daylight. Marlan says that all things are first created spiritually before they are physically manifest. . . Whatever, if I see those things again in my wide-awake world, and others are validating them as well, then I will be able to discern and understand them; and perhaps take appropriate action. . .)

The months of March and April, 1984 were critical times for the future of this planet. Colossal forces were locked in mortal combat. Enormous energies were centered in the Pacific Northwest, and overflowed to include much of Canada and the United States. Energies peaked between March 8th and April 8th. Most of the people slept unawares.

The secret combinations did not sleep in those days. Even the statue of liberty hid her face from America, except in dreams and visions.

Potential forces of terrible destruction were abroad in the land. Time held its breath for the outcome as the struggle drew to a frenzy, a critical point, a stalemate. Both sides paused, each with a sharp sword pressed tight to the other's jugular, and looked up for a higher choice, a decision to be made in the governing councils of the gods.

The people in the west walked like the dead they would have been in an instant if the gods had not held time in their hands, and had not stopped the clock for them. The aura of the people had lifted loose from their physical bodies; their days were numbered in seconds.

The limited vision of mortal man, working with a powerful mastermind of sorcery, witchcraft and forces from the lower spirit worlds, had attempted to steal time from the gods and to bring forth the new age by caesarian section. It would have been a stillborn child. God will not permit failure this time. . .

Those of you who care to research these events may gather clues from the media of those days. Search the newspapers of the northwestern cities and elsewhere. Look at videotapes of cable television programs. Look for stories that never happened. Search Sunday morning videos of the religious rings and see if they did not attempt to portray the Christ as a woman walking upon the earth.

See if you can find both wings, and the center, the operations of the legitimate priesthood as it moved to keep a delicate balance, yet not destroy either essential wing.

Look at the confusion on the tongue and in the face of the mouthpieces of the secret combinations as they attempted to display their magical powers on a Sunday morning, not knowing that a god would tune in, look upon their secret works, and deactivate the programming of their slaves and lifeform robots.

Interview people who sat in the audience on those occasions. People laughed at the feeble efforts, and were shocked at the foul language that came forth from the mouths of their respected evangelists as they failed to heal and to move the masses as before.

Toy with the lottery broadcasts. Look for the trap door, and the pillars of fire from below that control and manipulate results as the people sleep. Look for earthquakes, movements of troops, volcanos, black holes, huge masses hurtling through space, nuclear explosions, gigantic ransoms, massive thefts, and crap games that never happened.

Search for strange movements and bookings among airlines, charters, modes of transportation in March, April, and before as confusing messages were sent to those who were seeking the safety of refuges in Mexico and elsewhere. Examine banking and financial records for significant flows in currencies. Question the sources, new accounts; and look for payoffs.

Check the written messages, the microdots, the ghosting and static on weather and information channels, for coordinates and the results of votes made by power groups, colors and races, as to where the destruction would be centered, and which church was right. The unaltered media of those critical days of shadow, change, and judgement will record that rehearsals for the real birth of a new age were being carried out. . .

Should the physical cover up be too strong for your research resources, check the psychic records, the feelings and strange experiences of common people at that time; the stories of coincidences, unusual phenomena, heightened awareness, peculiar insights, visions of the dead, the cutting down of trees, accelerated learning.

Find the power spots, the City of Victory, the ancient temple sites that few suspect so far from where they had looked before. Question why people are at such locations. They know not except for a peculiar feeling inside. Discern between the power spots of each side, and look for the center where the gods will meet. Desire to be with them. . .

Watch for rehearsals again each year as power cycles peak about the sixth day of April. All will know without a doubt when the rehearsal is over, the veil is split, the drama is done. . .

Chapter Twenty-One

"I have cut off the nations; their towers are desolate; I made their streets waste, that none passeth by: their cities are destroyed, so that there is no man, that there is none inhabitant." Zephaniah 3:6

"For, behold, the Lord cometh out of his place to punish the inhabitants of the earth for their iniquity: the earth also shall disclose her blood, and shall no more cover her slain." Isaiah 26:21

In the days of Noah, the dark days of shadow and sudden change, a word of warning went out from the temples. But few ceased from the constant round of parties and riotous living.

As Noah built the ark for his family and those chosen from the animal kingdom, people who were touched on the one hand were disappearing from their homes, and from the face of the earth. Thus it was that when the floodgates were opened only the wicked remained upon the earth without the ark.

In the days of Enoch a temple and a city were taken, removed from the earth. John the beloved is said to have tarried and to walk yet upon this world. There are rumors of three more, and mysterious others also.

In the days of Noah a promise was extracted from the heavens. Never again would earth be baptized, cleansed from the pollutions of man, by immersion in water. A sign, the rainbow, was placed in the heavens in token of that covenant. It is said that in the year the rainbow appears in the sky there shall be no destruction by fire of an entire planet. Is it possible that in these days, the last days of shadow and sudden change, a new promise may be wrought from the gods?

Must those who remain reap the destruction hovering over their heads? Must the ears and hearts of the gods and the innocent be pierced again by the screams, the terror of millions of mothers, fathers, wives, children, caught in the flames, the awful inferno of a burning world?

Must monster earthquakes, the heaving of the seas beyond their bounds, whirlwinds, the falling down of mountains, wars, pestilence, the moon being bathed in blood, come to pass that even the sun must hide his head in shame and agony?

Is there a chance that the hand of the destroyer could yet be stayed? Could not those who have chosen be caught up to the city in the clouds, and those who remain continue with their lives? As in the days of Moses when an entire generation was lost in the wilderness, could it be that the new ones rising up would be just, and their fathers spared from the rod to live out their natural lives in the wilderness? Could the golden age be lived in another time or another place? Could those who are caught up choose peace for those who remain?

Or must earth herself be cleansed by fire from the pollutions already upon her? If so, could the wicked not die a natural death before the flames come? Or is it that when the righteous are removed from their midst the wicked will destroy themselves speedily?

Our logic fails us. We look up and appeal to a greater god. . .

Chapter Twenty-Two

"This kind of knowledge is a thing that comes in a moment like a light kindled from a leaping spark which, once it has reached the soul, finds its own fuel." Plato, B.C. 428

"The dead have looked upon the long absence of their spirits from their bodies as a bondage. Anxiously they awaited the morning of the first resurrection." Modern Scripture

From the garden in my backyard I look up and see two burning firebrands, two contrails together smoking across the sky. One pulses irregular puffs of smoke and they disappear behind a layer of cloud.

Through a circular hole I see them again, high and to the south. One tumbles through the hole and becomes a large ball, a sphere of white-blue pulsating energy. It flashes in a circle clockwise, then crashes on the towers of a city to the east. An inferno of sudden fire rises to a mushroom cloud. All clocks stop at 11:11 a.m.

As I fall to the earth behind a flimsy unpainted fence, I think once, hoping that my children are prepared for their dying. Then I am with myself; ready, meditating, feeling well. . .

We weep uncontrollably, fingers flying furiously; pushing buttons, assessing damage. Cold cathode-ray tubes beam with sudden fire, digital numbers spin dizzily. The flames. . .always the flames!

We were gods then, rulers of galaxies. But we lost a ship. We had technology, instruments, power. Yet we could not save them. Even now as I write this, great tears drown the pages and I cry deep uncontrolled sobbings. We could not even retrieve charred bodies to carry back with us to our home among the stars.

My well-beloved was on that ship. I shall return one day to this earth. I shall come alone, and find her again. . .I promise.

Chapter Twenty-Three

"The eternal parent wrapped in her ever invisible robes had slumbered once again for seven eternities. Time was not, for it lay asleep in the infinite bosom of duration. Universal mind was not, for there were no celestial beings to contain it. The seven ways to bliss were not. The great causes of misery were not, for there was no one to produce and get ensnared by them. Darkness alone filled the boundless all, for father, mother and son were once more one, and the son had not awakened yet for the new wheel, and his pilgrimage thereon." Book of Dzyan, B.C. 3000?

Consider, if you will, the very beginning when there was only god. You are that god. . .

You awaken as from a deep sleep, remembering vaguely that you slept to escape the endless boredom of an eternity of nothing. You lie on a bed, a warm, soft, comfortable bed; the bed upon which you were born, upon which you lived your life, upon which you died; you were born, you lived your life, you died.

You could get up, totter around a bit, eat, read the newspaper; but you've done all that before, and you never feel hunger anymore. So you lie there awake, looking at the ceiling, trying to remember what you were, who you were, why you were, why you awoke.

Nothing, nothing is fun, nothing has meaning. Did it ever? You try to sleep, but you've been there before. You awake, look at the ceiling, lie there, wonder vaguely why you awoke. . .

Slowly a hand rises from your side; your arm, your hand. As it passes before your eyes you see it strangely as though for the first time. Perhaps it is the first time you have seen an arm, a hand; was there ever another time when you saw an arm, a hand? You wonder why it won't go away, but it won't, it hangs there, floating in the air, between you and the ceiling. Your eyes focus on the hand, they learn to focus on the hand floating in the air, suspended between you and the ceiling.

Another hand rises from the other side of the bed; a hand and an arm. They meet in the air, touching, caressing, gently exploring each other; wondering why and who they are. You see them suspended between you and the ceiling. You see for the first time that the ceiling is plastered, sprayed on. It has thousands of tiny holes, contours, shapes, forms, shadows.

You note the alignment, the coordinates your clasped hands and arms make with the holes, the contours, shapes, forms, shadows. You see a hair on your hands, another, and many on your hands, your arms. You note the coordinates of each hair with each hole, contour, shape, form, shadow.

The hair moves, stands on end, coordinates change with the arc. Stonehenge is born! Clasped hands rise above your head forming a circle; the sign of the coming of the son of man is given! You feel a sound rising from your chest, it splits your lips, forms a word, sounds a trumpet; you are that word. . .

She looks at you strangely; waiting, forgetting whose move it is. You remember now, Stella and you were playing a game. It was her game. You've always played the game; it never began, it never ended, it always was. It's her move, and you wait as she forgets whose move it is. You know how Stella is, you can't tell her it's her move. . .

Who is Stella? How did she get here? Who are you? As you wait for Stella to forget whose move it is, you remember that it's her game. She hurt you the last time she took you out. You awoke with a bloody lip. . .

Then you remember; it was your game, it was her move. She awoke with the bloody lip. You weren't gentle when you made love. You told her you would always make love gently, but she must be gentle when she takes you out of another body. You wanted to come out awake and aware, that was the deal; but gently, gently. . .

She got even. It was her game. She played god again; made the worlds, the people, the animals, all the same as before. She made you Satan, and left you there in hell. It was supposed to be a game, it was supposed to be fun, but she left you there, she didn't come back to take you out. And it hurt, it really really hurt down there. And she didn't come back, and she didn't come back, and it hurt, and it hurt, and hurt, and hurt; and she had promised to be gentle, and you had promised to be gentle, and it was fun to play; but she left you there; and it hurt, it hurt like hell. . .

You tell Stella never to put you on the wheel again, promise, never, forever. . .

But you know that every game must be better than the last, or you will awake as if from a deep sleep remembering vaguely that you slept to escape the endless boredom of an eternity of nothing. You lie on a bed, a warm, soft, comfortable bed; the bed upon which you were born, lived, died; you feel hunger no more, you've done all that before, a hand rises, an arm, another hand, an arm; they meet, caress, explore, make love. You note the hair. . .

Then you remember the people, the children, the mothers, fathers; their joys, sorrows, good times, hopes, dreams, blue skies, white clouds, sunshine, the big bang, the universe exploding outwards, the impossible problem, the god game, the wheel, Stella, who are you, the universe will collapse if someone, anyone, stops playing the game. They're counting on you, you, *YOU*! Only you can save it all; and you can't remember, Stella can't remember, whose move it is now.

And she left you there because you weren't gentle when you made love; and it's her game, no it's your game; and you can't remember, she can't remember whose move it is now. . .

Through the ceiling you hear a sound, the scraping of a chair being pushed back; the sound of someone rising from a long sitting.

You know then that in the room above you there is another bed, another god, and another floor, another story on top of that one, and another, and another, and each god in each story is playing a bigger and bigger game. For each there are more hands, more arms, more holes, contours, shapes, forms, shadows; more people, animals, hairs. . .

And then and only then do you remember that it was Stella's game, your move. You remember how you found the impossible clue. The game was trivial pursuit. They were playing at the Cherry Bank Hotel; the airplane said so. The stone was under a tree at Laurel Point. You heard tortoise, hare, the year of the hare. The flat tire was on the Toyota, the people, Volkswagen Rabbit, was between the blue Toyota and the Station Wagon. The name of the game was *"Not A Hair Shall Be Lost"*. . .

The clue was in the belly of a dead earthworm that clung voluntarily to a tiny spark of life; crucified, crushed on the side of a path, near a park bench, on a world; for seven days so it could move with the precisely perfect infinitesimally small movement that would give the final clue, the coordinates to reveal the last hair that the gods must find, or be found a liar, cease to be god, have everything rush back in on itself, cease to be, and awake, lying there, looking at the ceiling, trying to remember. . .

In the room below you hear the sound of running water. You have trained them well, the ones below. You knew them well. Every tiny movement of every microbe, every particle of dust; every hair, every moment in eons of time within their systems was perfectly predictable. You left them clues too for the next game, the next time the lowest young god would need to create new space. They learned well, as had

63

you, the value of the lowest of lifeforms. And they send love and gentleness to all those who serve behind. . .

Everything has a purpose, nothing happens by accident.

You get out of bed, open the drapes, the glass door, step out onto the balcony, watch the signs in the raven, the gull, the dove, see that the green leaves are out, the flowers open. Somewhere a car engine starts, then another, and another. People frozen like statues of salt come to life, move, yawn, smile, go about their business.

Two seagulls, lovers, are locked in bronze; frozen with the eagle, the bear, the wolf, another. A sorcerer's spell is cast. Seals are placed before Caesar's temple.

You know that somewhere, somewhere in a penthouse far above you, the highest god has started the clock again.

Or was it the worm. . .?

You know that the wheel has slowed for the people; that there is new space, new time, an eighth star in the Pleiades; a larger ark safely docked than before; a going eastward from Eden one kilometer, a return of fifteen hundred meters. A good gain!

You breathe in and breathe out, the breath of life is in your nostrils. The gods have decreed that the people remember no more the six hours, the six days when they were forced to play God.

As the worm turns so do the worlds go 'round. Thanks Kira for getting us down to earth again!

But was it the serpent, the worm, (*"I wish you joy o' the worm Cleopatra"*) who tempted Eve to tempt Adam?

Or was it Adam, or god, who tempted the serpent to tempt Eve to tempt Adam? Whose move was it anyway?

But let's rest from our labors now for a little season, or forever continue in circles going round, and going round, and round, and round, and that's past business. We've been there already. Isn't that so. . .?

Chapter Twenty-Four

"The chess-board is the world, the pieces are the phenomena of the universe, the rules of the game are what we call the laws of Nature. The player on the other side is hidden from us." Thomas Huxley, 1825-1895

"But there shall not an hair of your head perish." Luke 21:18

The circles, the equations, the chains of associations that magic words awaken in the broadly educated mind, generate the heat, the momentum, the intense energy that is needed to explode a mortal consciousness, or a world, into supermortal accelerated learning, and a close encounter with the gods. Once this level of energy, synergy, has been reached awake and aware, it is difficult for the human mind to ever be the same again.

The computer exercise, the god game described above is child's play to the potential intelligence of the human mind. There is no place in the universe that your mind is not capable of penetrating. Indeed, *"not a hair shall be lost"*!

Be warned however that it is a terrible experience to be on the wheel, and to make the change that eventually you will make anyway. . .

The operational rule is: *"There are many springs and many summers; sometimes it is more fun to just - float!"*

Choose for yourself which spring and which summer will be the season of your becoming. Avoid the boredom of past business which is old learning. Learn to discern between fear and love, and which is motivating you.

Are you going toward something because you love it; or are you going away from something because you fear it? Is it possible to choose to love everything? Is there anything in the universe to fear, or only things to be understood?

Have fun with your life and learning in a correct way. Or, choose to float if you are content with life as it is now. Floating can be lovely. It prolongs the agony exquisitely!

The rings of magic are still not accustomed to me in my newly adopted city along the sea. Last week I partook of the sun, lying on the grass beside the walls of an old Indian fortification.

I took delight in watching a young mother attempt to fly a kite with her son. She was a childwoman. From a distance she would pass for a child. She moved and played as a child; her short blonde hair gracefully flowing in a festival of harmony with the lithe movements of her limbs. Her smiles danced with delight as the kite rose bobbing on warm currents of air rushing before the waves of the sea.

She seemed intensely aware of my interest. Later, as I sat in my car she walked by. Our eyes met and sang songs of mutual appreciation.

The rings took my delight for desire. Yesterday I sat on a bench in a square, curious to see how the rings would move in that location. Soon a man with a red tam came by, walking erratically, stopping, turning around, pacing a few steps, then returning. He left, walking eastward.

Perhaps fifteen minutes later, in my car I moved south. Within two blocks the man with the red tam appeared and slowed traffic for a moment as he seemed about to stagger across the street. I knew he was establishing spacetime coordinates for another.

Within fifty feet I saw the childwoman walking by herself. I saw the opportunity to park the car, approach her, and establish a relationship. I kept going. Within the hour, many blocks away she was presented again, three feet behind me in a supermarket lineup. I went to my car. She passed by soon, confused that I sought her not. . .

Yes, I feel the emotions: lonely, hurt, hurtful, hurting. The discipline of the ancient priesthood is strict. It is in the world but cannot be of it. There was a time when it was not lawful for the sons of god to pair off with the daughters of men. Perhaps the methods are more refined now?

Who can be all things for all people? Who can bleed for everyone; satisfy all needs, all desires, unravel all magic, undo all karma, balance mercy and justice, reconcile the two brothers? It is not I. You look for another. . .

Chapter Twenty-Five

"The Valley Spirit never dies. It is called the Mysterious Female. And the doorway of the Mysterious Female is the base from which Heaven and Earth spring. It is there within us all the time. Draw upon it as you will, it never runs dry." Lao-Tzu, B.C. 600

In this world, Kira and I are seldom physically together. Should we need to be we are in an instant. Kira has a different work to perform. She moves among a wide spectrum of people. At this level even I may have to look closely to discover her disguise.

Being female energy, Kira has been trained to closely observe human life; to be constantly aware of the movements of magic as they affect her, her world, and the people around her. We remain in constant touch through our own private channel of communication. To walk upon this earth we have chosen to shut down some of our faculties; and even for a time, to forget. . .

Observe the female children. Watch how from their childhood they look closely at other people; how others walk, dress, move, talk, think. Women are masters of delicate movement, the interpretation of the body language of the soul; experts in reading the lower mind levels of each other, and of the male.

Such is their code, their sisterhood, the reason why they seek out each other for moments of intimate sharing that are not open to the adult male.

Women can predict with accuracy the motor movements of the male, and therefore manipulate and motivate with skill. There is little in a man that can be hid from the probing eyes and mind of a woman. . .

Nature, the gods, have fashioned a balance. Few women allow themselves to become aware that although they may accurately read the male process leading to a final decision, and may even track that process through his tentative choices; at that point they withdraw into themselves and feel how that decision will affect their own lives.

Women are therefore usually shut out from the final decision; unless the male choses to reveal it.

The bottom line of creation is that there must always be a greater god. The final decision rests with the male energy. That property alone is the only difference between the sexes in the creative process as viewed by the gods.

Sex on the physical plane is a symbolic representation of the creation of worlds, galaxies, spirit increase. This is recognized in the traditional restrictions placed upon sexual relations, and in the heightened awareness that comes in moments when the sexual act transcends the physical level.

The father/mother family role is the physical teaching/learning experience most resembling the role of God.

Chapter Twenty-Six

"The tendency of modern physics is to resolve the whole material universe into waves, and nothing but waves. These are waves of two kinds: bottled up waves which we call matter, and unbottled waves which we call radiation or light. If annihilation of matter occurs, the process is merely that of unbottling imprisoned wave energy and letting it fall to travel through space. These concepts reduce the whole universe to a world of light; potential and existent, so that the whole story of creation can be told with perfect accuracy and completeness in the six words: "God said, "Let there be light.""" Sir James Jeans

Consider, if you will, the highest Gods meeting in a grand governing council at the very center of the universe. The problem before them is the provision of new learning experiences for the evolution of consciousness at all levels. A bold new possibility is being considered; one which has never before been tried.

The entire universe has been constructed upon a balance of matter and antimatter. It has been created in the form of a circle, a ring; or perhaps more correctly, a sphere, a perfect sphere.

From the beginning as one particle of matter has been created, simultaneously a particle of antimatter has appeared on the other half of the ring. Patterned after this fashion, numberless smaller rings have evolved within the whole; each being coordinated to a perfect balance by the master plan and the hierarchy set up for that purpose. You may picture this perhaps like the concentric skins of an onion, or maybe Ezekiel's *"wheel within a wheel"*. . .

To this point the universe has been expanding outward from the original center where the big bang occurred. Now the council has determined that the bounds set for the universe have been reached. A perfect form has evolved in accordance with the pattern established by the original master plan. Any further expansion would result in deformities, and in the unthinkable intrusion upon the space of the Unknown God who provided the master plan and set its bounds and limits.

The perfect universal form that has been reached is nonetheless a duality. Matter and antimatter, male and female, sense constantly their incompleteness without the other. The people feel hollow inside. They search continuously for something, some unknown, some missing part of themselves. They walk about touching others, pretending that another is dreaming the same dream, knowing their need for a complete relationship, a perfect eternal companion, a total fulfillment of themselves.

They search, not knowing that a perfect shadow, a perfect counterpart is dreaming their dream; but on the other side of the ring.

You cannot hold your shadow in your arms. You cannot be fulfilled without the union of matter and antimatter. . .

The council has decided that there is only one way to expand further, and to allow everyone to have that which they most desire; a complete relationship with themselves.

All calculations have been made. The combined intelligence of all lifeforms in the universe; residing in the mind of the chairman of the council, the oldest God; has determined that there is an excellent chance of success, but an element of risk involved in the new plan. Because of the risk, all gods, all rings of power, must vote before the plan can be put into operation.

The plan is to allow the universe to collapse back in upon itself to the center. The task is to ensure that a perfect balance of both forces remains right to the moment of fusion. If the timing is perfect, the coordinates precise, an explosion of unknown dimensions will occur.

It has been determined that the collision of a perfect balance of all known matter and antimatter will result in light. Light has always been known to be the result of ascendent and desirable forces of evolution. Perhaps, the Gods reasoned, with the creation of our galaxies and star systems we have simply been rehearsing for this moment to collapse the entire universe.

Such an event had never been known before; even to the oldest God. In effect, all dense creations, all worlds of illusion, all physical matter in its present form, would be destroyed.

Would consciousness survive? Would there be a complete relationship as shadow mingled intimately with shadow?

Excited as they were, none of the Gods noticed the sparkle in the eye of the oldest God as he and his lovely companion left the council chambers to retire to their quarters for the night. . .

The choices had been made, the votes were in from all organized space. Already the collapse had begun. The chairman, the highest intelligence, watched all movements from the council chambers at the exact center of the universe.

From the outposts the delicate fabric of creation began to fold. It created a colossal wind which pushed everything ahead of it. Nothing could resist its movement. Planets were tossed like cotton balls in a tornado. Suns were sucked in as dust in the mouth of a hurricane. Already gods were calling up the line to Gods for assurance, and for help with coordinates and balance.

Once started, everything seemed to happen so fast, and seemed so final. The Gods sneaked glances at the chairman to ensure his composure was real. They wondered now, knowing they could not reverse the process, if they had made a mistake. They had placed everything in the final decision, the final logic of the chairman. They had trusted him completely with all their creations.

Had he been testing them as young gods were tested to see if they would make a mistake, a wrong choice? Had they created this destruction themselves, and the chairman went along with it out of boredom with his own existence? As the universe folded, doubts flew fast in the council chambers.

Galaxies crashed into galaxies, system into system. The cries, the awful sound of billions of lifeforms extinguished together, usually heard from burning worlds, never did arrive at the center. Few knew by then what they had really voted in favor of. All had trusted another above; knowing that intelligence increased with position in the hierarchy.

Surely god, or surely God, or surely the chairman, knew what he was doing. . .?

The Gods would talk later of how the chairman and his companion held hands linked closely to each other as the final moment arrived for the center. They would talk about the mysterious door that appeared in the center of the council chambers; a door that looked like a polished sea of glass, spun perhaps from pure gold. They noted the reflection of the chairman and his companion in the door. The tale would be told that at the very end, just before the door opened, their clasped hands formed a sphere, a perfect sphere. . .

The second oldest God was elected chairman of the grand governing council, by acclamation. He was more intelligent than all the others put together.

The members of the council, the Gods, had never before been known to sleep and to dream while they were on duty at the center. They found they had dreamed the same dream. They checked with gods in their system and found that none had heard of a new plan, or of a vote being called. The universe appeared to be the same. The only validation for the council was that the former chairman and his companion had disappeared without a trace.

The second oldest God, the new chairman, was the only one who had been close enough to peek through the golden door. What he saw there was never shared with anyone, ever. . .

Chapter Twenty-Seven

"So God created man in his own image, in the image of God created he him; male and female created he them." Genesis 1:27

"There shall be time no longer. But in the days of the seventh angel, when he shall begin to sound, the mystery of God should be finished." Revelation 10:6,7

It is written that on the fifth day of creation the gods made the fowls of the air, and the fishes of the sea. On the sixth day they made the beasts of the field. In that day God also made man. Let us consider, if you will, that sixth day as it may have happened at the center.

It is the morning of the sixth day of creation. A trumpet sounds a clear and certain signal, a word, through the universe to call the gods of creation home. Many times it has been rehearsed before, but only at the precise moment of its maturity can the trumpet sound the exact note that will bring the gods from their hiding place among the stars. In the air and in the seas the fowl and the fish begin their annual migration.

Only the most alert sentinel, one whose eyes would never blink from the screen, could have detected the faint trace that would have given away the position of the tiny spacecraft as it hurtled suddenly from a planet close to the star Kobol.

The three gods aboard the craft were highly skilled in deploying evasive tactics to hide their tracks and coordinates from an enemy that sought to find and to destroy the race of man. That enemy could never be allowed to discover the secret of how the gods multiplied. Always for the enemy there had to be left, a missing link. No mistakes had ever been made before, none could be allowed to happen now.

The gods felt the tremendous burden that rested upon their shoulders. Theirs was a mission to bring a royal child home. Each had been programmed and trained for eons of time to accomplish specific tasks for this mission. Only one, the pilot, was programmed for them all. Only he was aware of that.

Never before had this mobile team of three been trusted together with such a task.

They knew they were venturing into a wasteland, a deadly hostile space inhabited by intelligent forces that would kill without mercy, and stamp out or steal everything the Gods had created and become since life began. God would cease to be God if this trio failed. The ascendent evolution of consciousness would terminate, the universe begin to collapse and rush back into itself as its very lifeforce was destroyed.

In the earthyear 1908 there were strange reports of a spacecraft in trouble. In flames it hurtled across Europe as the pilot strove desperately to maintain altitude, and to guide it beyond the inhabited areas of earth.

The three voyagers from deep space knew that an unknown enemy had placed a fault in their craft's design, and that a nuclear explosion was about to occur. Close to Kamchatka, they abandoned their ship to its destiny.

Only the pilot survived. He alone walked the earth as god. He knew that, hopeless as it seemed without his lost instruments, even though he might yet find the child, he could never return unless a greater god trained and sent another mission, a better vehicle, to the rescue.

The timing was in their hands!

Alone, in hopeless anguish over the loss of his two companions, and the impossible failure of their mission, he wept bitterly. Then he began to do the one thing he had power to do in an impossible attempt to retrieve what was lost. He put one foot in front of the other, leaned forward a bit to defy gravity, and took one single solitary step into the darkness. . .

The probing eyes of enemy spacecraft made it impossible for the gods to increase in all known space without risk of detection. For many generations they had secretly implanted their seed within the bodies of animals.

The enemy was not aware of this. The instruments of their scouting ships would reveal only a planet with no intelligent lifeforms beyond that of the animal kingdom. Yet, hidden somewhere within the body of a single hare, was the cluster of cells, the royal child that the pilot sought.

Knowledgeable in the history of the planet, the pilot thought of how closely his own unbroken stream of consciousness had followed that of David of the Old Testament record.

As a lonely shepherd on the hills, David had acquired the habit of deep meditation, and reflection upon the meaning of life. The pilot had spent many years as a deep space commander on lonely outposts far from his home planet. He too had formed the habit of deep reflection. His soldiers had often come for advice and counsel with their personal problems, and he had needed to think deeply about the implications of the counsel he gave the soldiers and officers for the lives of their wives, children, and generations unborn.

Like David, the pilot had spent much time among the governing

73

circles of his home world, and was trained in self-control and generosity toward others. Later, as part of a rebellion against corruption in government, the pilot had learned much about power and the lower depths of men. He too had become guilty of grave crimes and sins against the former laws and the order he had previously fought others to preserve.

Yet always, David and the pilot knew deep inside that there was a greater god than themselves. Inside the golden temple of his advanced years, the pilot, by then a king in his own right, had also become a high priest, and a god.

David led Israel through their golden years. But because of his sin against Uriah, his soul was condemned to hell. The god of David, however, indicated that he might not leave David's soul to burn in hell forever. As the pilot took another step forward into the darkness of his own hell, he took comfort that maybe he too would one day be rescued by a greater god. . .

The mother hare was unaware of the cluster of alien cells that had been implanted deep within her body when the gnat had entered her ear. She, like the other animals, had lived peacefully in an abundant garden for as long as they could remember. There were some vague stirrings within when she heard old stories of how the two-legged gods of creation had come, hundreds of years before, in chariots of fire thundering from the skies. But she was content to go about the business of living her own life among friends.

The implant had removed only a few unused brain cells, and had migrated in a small cluster grouped about a queen cell, to an area within the heart of the hare. The gnat had departed, having fulfilled its programming.

Unknown to the queen, the gnat had left a master cell in the brain. Over the years this master cell, lonely and giving up all hope for rescue by his own kind, had mated with a female cell of the hare. They produced seven offspring which migrated and circulated throughout the system of the hare.

On the morning of a certain day, the wind whispered a magic word in the ear of the hare. Her heart leaped within her.

The alien queen suddenly remembered that it was her turn in a game she was playing. She remembered her promise to rescue the master cell from the lonely hell she had left him in.

Mobilizing her forces with keys and passwords; ancient coordinates remembered from the migration between brain and heart; the queen sent out a task force to rescue the master and bring him home to the center.

The task force went out and returned weak and failing. Things had changed. There were enemies at every turn of the way, monster cells that would eat them alive if they weren't aware and faster in their movements. The queen sent out a poison that slowed the heartbeat, and the hare slept. In the silence they heard the call of the male and listened for his coordinates.

In sleep the hare's system was slowed even further. The worker cells found the master, and led him to the center.

The queen commanded the sealing of the line to their throne; but the master went out again. With the workers he searched the whole system; fighting off enemy cells at every turn. They brought in the seven children.

Such a thing had never been known to happen before. It defied all programming. The master cell, after mating with a lower consciousness, had thought for itself. The master had shown love for the illegitimate children, and refused to leave them behind.

The workers had exhausted their programming now. They died as the channel, the conduit to the center, was sealed. The hare awoke. The master and the queen merged as one. Now there was a live cluster of eight in the center. . .

Old Indian legends tell how the gods came from the *"seven sisters"* in the Pleiades. The Sioux nation talk of *"taku wakan skan skan"*; something holy moving among the stars. They talk of Mu and Atlantis. They tell how the hare was given her long legs and speed to escape her enemies, in exchange for her favor to the gods.

Legends relate how other animals and fowl: raven, dove, bear, wolf, spider, who helped with creation, were given some of the attributes of a god in exchange. The Red Man talks of the sacred eagle, the four directions, the pipe, the unity of all things; and gives respect to mother earth, father sky, and all their creations.

Could it be that the master plan calls for a raising of consciousness at all levels when a new child is born to the Gods? Could it be that with the splitting of a world an entity with the intelligence of a gnat might rise comparatively to that of a hare; and the hare to the awareness of a man who uses only five percent of his brain capacity?

Could it be that the gods always leave behind an improvement, a better vehicle?

Perhaps when the hare had received her reward, the next implant was made in a larger vehicle; maybe in the body of a reindeer. Perhaps the gods touched that reindeer with a mark that they alone would recognize. Maybe it was a warm red glow that they could watch from the stars while they waited for the gestation period of a new world to be complete.

At the right time the gods of creation would return. The light of their coming would be as a new star in the heavens. Together with the littlest reindeer leading all others of that species, they would fly through the heavens bearing new gifts, gifts of love to all the children. . .

Chapter Twenty-Eight

"The present hour is the descending God, and all things obey; all the past exists to it as subordinate; all the future is contained in it. . ."
Emerson's Journal

"You must become as a little child to enter the kingdom of God." Luke 18:17

"Where children are, there is the golden age." Novalis 1772-1801

The fairy tales, the stories your children love, have purpose and meaning. No creative effort is without a higher purpose. Nothing happens by accident.

Have you forgotten how to play; how to take delight in simple things as the little ones do? Have you forgotten that you can manifest all things you desire by flying on the wings of your imagination? Do you not recall that children when they play do not dream alone as you do? They play together in a small flexible reality that is much more real than the constant stress of adult pretensions to conformity.

When a split is made in a world, a god has to descend to pull the consciousness of lower lifeforms to a higher level of awareness. It is always a game that includes some element of risk. It has never been done before with the personality and experience of that descending god, and that particular group of lifeforms. It is up to the god to choose how low he can go, and still get back with his burden of new souls.

Perhaps this can be better understood by thinking of a god as an entity vibrating at a very high frequency. Should the high resonance not be stepped down or buffered before contact with lifeforms vibrating at lower rates, it would burn them up. Or, to use our former analogy, bind them to a spinning wheel.

The purpose of making a split is to raise the vibrations of all lifeforms associated with that planet, including the planet itself, to the highest level they are capable of reaching without causing psychological destruction, or undue trauma. The destruction of physical vehicles may in some instances be in the best evolutionary interests of some entities, and necessary to preserve a balance for them.

Physical destruction, or alteration and wide awake change, is determined by the lifestyle each lifeform has chosen during the gestation period.

When the time has arrived for fission; the choices, the judgements, are already in and higher laws prevail over physical. The energies of the descending god are the catalyst to effect synergy on a global basis, and to bring in the new age.

We suggest you study the prophetic scriptures. There need be no surprises for you. All things were known and recorded from the beginning. Some records were hidden, but are now being revealed as witnesses and warnings from the fathers to the children.

Look too for modern temples. They are here and you know them not. The temples are staffed by the same priesthood that invited Kira and I to our glorious golden voyage.

From these temples teachers go out, two by two, with a golden record under their arm, a voice of warning, and a message that a marvelous work and a wonder is happening among the people. Within the walls of modern temples, the highest councils have authorized the sealing of eternal dyads.

All choices are yet, for a time, yours. . .

Chapter Twenty-Nine

"Whatsoever things are true, whatsoever things are honest, whatsoever things are pure, whatsoever things are lovely, whatsoever things are of good report; if there be any virtue, and if there be any praise, think on these things. And the peace of God, which passeth all understanding, shall keep your hearts and minds." Philippians 4:7,8

"There are also celestial bodies, and bodies terrestrial; but the glory of the celestial is one, and the glory of the terrestrial is another." 1 Corinthians 15:40

"And before the throne there was a sea of glass like unto crystal. . ." Revelation 4:6

Consider, if you will, that there exists in the universe a long chain of planets of different orders.

We will call the present level of the planet upon which we stand, *"telestial"*. The next planet above ours is a golden planet at level two. We'll call it *"terrestrial"*. The third highest planet, at level three is like a sea of glass. It is called *"celestial"*.

Above these are worlds of even higher orders, and higher states of glory. Below telestial are lesser evolved worlds upon which animal, or plant, or mineral lifeforms are currently the dominant form of intelligence. Each planet vibrates at a rate that will sustain the quality of life that exists upon it.

Upon each planet where several orders of organized life coexist, lower lifeforms are buffered from higher vibrations by a *"veil"* which emanates from the group consciousness of the stream of intelligence next above it.

Upon earth at level one, the veil for animal life; and thus the extent of the animal kingdom's progress; emanates from the combined thoughts and expressions of the race of man.

For plants, the animal kingdom presides. Minerals are dependent upon the plant kingdom for purification, and the next evolutionary step upward in the chain of consciousness that begins in the primordial sea of elemental intelligence.

The process of growth and purification is assisted by rings of beings which move within the rainbow colored veils. In the body of man, all kingdoms are represented.

Each order of planet spins at a rate which determines the times and seasons thereon. The direction of spin may change from time to time, or may appear to change should the poles reverse.

Each planet is surrounded by an aura of light, its glory, that varies in quality and intensity with the prevailing group consciousness of the dominant lifeform thereon. Planet earth at level one is seen to have an aura comparable to the light now received on earth from the stars. Using the same analogy as scale, a level two planet appears to the gods as a being whose aura can be compared to the light received from the full moon. Level three has the glory of the sun.

Should a planet be forced from its orbit and flee through space, it might approach a star which is a sun of greater magnitude than the one in its former solar system.

The light of the gods is the glory of the sun. Could earth have fallen from another group of stars? Shall she return?

As the golden age approaches, this planet is preparing to shift to a level two order. A level two world spins at a different vibratory rate. It may be for example that a hundred years at level one would be one day at level two. Perhaps a thousand years at level one is a single day on a level three order. Consider the possibilities if it is so. . .

Those who have not yet prepared their minds to function at level two vibrations would be put on a wheel should they be suddenly snatched to the higher order. It is necessary for them to learn more at level one; to prepare for another spring and another summer somewhere in time. They have made their choice. The votes, the judgements, the desires are all in before the split is complete. They have been ensnared by carnal thoughts and things. They have chosen to elevate their mind and thoughts to higher levels more slowly, upon a lesser world; such as earth is now at level one.

Consider that the split is made. The chain advances one notch. The planet below earth moves up to level one and man appears upon it. The new level one planet may be stocked from those who could not abide the glorious coming of the descending god. It could also be stocked from other sources. It too must conform to the master plan. It will have its garden, its Adam and Eve, its Satan, and perhaps its Christ as well. The new level one planet's angels and gods may be those who have now evolved awake and aware to level two, the golden planet of peace, rest, and fulfillment.

We are in the golden age. Earth has evolved to a level two glory. Those left in the space behind may one day have their own level two glory. At that time, or perhaps on a different circle, we will be lifted one notch and reach our level three. It may be that to reach level three we must first pull those who so choose on level one, to level two where we are. Perhaps the same rules apply throughout the chain and the ascendent arc could actually be viewed as a pyramid.

Now, awake and aware at level two, we can fly! Our physical bodies can do what only the astral could when we lived on a level one planet. Through our own curiosity, our own efforts, we have followed the path of *"Jonathan Livingston Seagull"* to the point where we can appear and disappear at will.

The aging process has been altered and we are a race of superbeings. To people on level one we are like those who went out from the temples of Mu as masters of matter to teach of things to come.

We have instruction and learning. Not all are permitted to minister visibly beyond the bounds of our own sphere. All things that took place on level one are revealed to us. We communicate without words if we choose. There is peace and abundant life. We no sooner desire something than it is physically manifest. We have no need for money or for labor at that which does not satisfy. We eat if we choose, or abstain from food and drink, it matters not. We take joy in our paradise world. The golden age is no longer just a dream; the master has appeared and dwells in our midst. . .

Consider the difference in the times, the rate of spin between our level two glory and that of those on level one. Should a hundred years there be only a day to us, we could walk a day invisible on their world and experience a hundred years of vicarious learning through our observations of others. We move from New York to London in the flick of an eye. We predict people's movements with accuracy. We move back and forth through their time. We could pause at a camp of Gypsies in the night, dance once around their campfire, and create a legend that would be told to babes for hundreds of years. . .

Invisible to us as we are to those at level one, we know that others, those from level three, are watching and learning from us.

It is said that those on level three are awake and aware to the Gods who dwell in their midst. Their planet at level three is a sphere, a perfect sphere, like a sea of glass spun from pure gold. As they walk upon it they look into its crystal depths and watch the movements of planets and people of a lower order. It is said that some, the initiates of an ancient order, eternal dyads, those on the way to be Gods, are given a white stone. In the stone's depths they see planets of a higher order.

Could it be that planets at level one and two are inside a sphere? Could the sphere be the head of a much larger body?

At our golden level two we have a thousand years to enjoy peace and rest. As the millennium draws to a close, we will pass though a short period of shadow and sudden change; a period of sifting and choices for a new split, a giant leap from level two to level three. The seeds and programming for that second split are already being sown.

During that short period, the gods and Gods will play their peculiar game again, and some may be bound to a spinning wheel as they create new space, new worlds, new star systems for themselves.

Could it be that when the Gods cease to play, all worlds rest? Could the golden age be a time when the clocks of the Gods stop; the games of men cease, and all people awake and aware become as the gods?

Perhaps someone somewhere pulls the plug on the master television set, and puts it away carefully, behind a closet door!

Chapter Thirty

"But thou, when thou prayest, enter into thy closet, and when thou hast shut thy door, pray to thy Father which is in secret; and thy Father which seeth in secret shall reward thee openly." Matthew 6:6

"The object and design of our existence is happiness." Joseph Smith, 1805-1844

"Scrutinize the mystery underlying all things. Seek in higher dimensions of understanding a meaning behind all our suffering. Unmask what appears to be the caprice of human destiny; how we long to become that which we hardly believe we are." Pir Vilayat Inayat Khan

Like Job of the Old Testament, have you been a righteous man as you walked your days upon the earth? Has an enemy sown tares in your fields as your watchman slept while you prayed in the garden? Has that which you most desired been taken from you by another?

It shall be restored manyfold. . .

Have you embarked upon a path of life, perhaps a business venture that failed because of others? Have your hopes, your fondest dreams and desires, been dashed by the politics, the economics, the education, the dishonesty, the snares of the secret combinations of your society? Have you felt hopeless and helpless in defeat, knowing your own righteousness before god? Have others misunderstood and judged you wrongly; offering swelling words and theories to make you as they are? Have you known a greater god all the days of your life, walked to the beat of a different drum?

You shall have all restored to you as at first you desired. Others will fulfill the success of your business venture unto the third and fourth generation of them that slept. It is their karma, their desire for recompense. The fruits shall be in the hands of your posterity.

By their fruits shall ye know those that went before. You shall beam with joy as you see your own children, your seed, blessed and prospered upon the face of the earth. They can do no wrong. They are safe, folded into your bosom.

Every desire of every individual shall be fulfilled, somewhere in time.

Chapter Thirty-One

"You cannot teach a man anything; you can only help him to find it within himself." Galileo, 1564-1642

"Few in the world can understand teaching without words, and the advantage of taking no action." Lao-Tzu, B.C. 600

In past dispensations, with some exceptions, communication from spirit levels surfaced through techniques such as automatic writing and trance mediumship. In most cases the channel was not consciously aware of what was going to take place, or the extent of the message.

Some fine uplifting works have come through when channels were attuned to higher levels of the hierarchy. However, it is easy to become ensnared in details of peoples and systems that are normally beyond the veil of this world; for a wise purpose in the master plan.

We note too the inspired works of the great composers, writers, painters, sculptors, singers, performers, artists of all description who have been moved upon by *"the muse"*.

Common themes often surface in all creative works within certain streams of time. Perhaps artists encounter the same muse as their contemporaries.

New age energies are patterned to raise awareness so that inspiration from high levels can come through all people awake and aware in the physical state. The goal is to remove the veil completely so that in the golden age, mortals may walk and talk with angels and gods awake and aware as they now do with people in the daylight world. With the veil of the heavens split open, knowledge will pour through so that all people can learn in a day what it may take a hundred years to comprehend at level one.

Even now as you talk with another, you are communicating at many different levels simultaneously. You may learn to tune in to those higher levels, and to obtain information from each other by asking questions that elicit the data you need from the other person's subconscious memory banks.

When you begin to communicate in such a manner, you may notice some ill-ease. The method is considered unusual by the other person. With practise between two people, you may develop to the point where no words need to be spoken at all.

It is said that among the American Indians in times past, a

grandfather would walk with a boy through the fields. No words would be spoken between them. Yet the boy will have learned from the grandfather who had been programming/teaching him from higher levels; even as I taught the dolphins.

We will teach you a game, a technique, a psychology whereby you may develop such skills if you desire. The secret is to listen with the throat instead of the ears!

We have already discussed levels of communication. You may set up points of reference to know at what level your awareness is presently centered.

For example, if you are consciously aware of the operation of one of the five physical senses, you know that your attention is centered at level one, the basic physical plane of communication. If you are aware of an emotion, you know that you are operating at level two. If you are centered upon a thought, you may use that as a point of reference that you are then operating at level three, the mental plane of communication. If you are aware of something beyond these points of reference, you are somewhere else.

By consciously discerning and using such points of reference as coordinates, you will quickly become aware not only of the three basic choice levels in your being, but also of the fact that *"you"* are really somewhere else. You will begin to know yourself. . .

Also, by establishing these points of reference, you will be able to gain mastery over your lower nature. For example, you sense an overpowering emotion, anger perhaps. Your trained mind determines that you are then operating at level two; nothing more, nothing less. You know your own nature, your span of consciousness flows also through level two. Should you choose not to have that emotion, shift levels. Should you choose to indulge in that emotion, you are.

You may shift levels by a variety of techniques. It is common for a beginner to use a physical movement; perhaps forming a circle with a thumb and forefinger, or consciously blinking an eyelid. You may thus choose which level you care to be at at any time, and no level has mastery over you.

You identify with higher levels of mind and begin to be useful to a ring or hierarchy to which you have already been programmed. The correct question to elicit information from another comes out of your mouth. You hear what you need to know in the words spoken in response to your question. You are beginning to be a *"Jedi Knight"*, a master of lower lifeforce. You have already earned belts and colors!

Again, we warn you that when you begin to consciously apply techniques like those described above, you will make changes that may be difficult to reverse. Once you see the world with higher faculties open, and remain in conscious touch with level one as well, the world may never again be the same for you.

You become aware of illusion. Things that formerly had much meaning for you no longer do. Will your family, friends, employers, psychologist, be able to accept sudden changes in your personality?

Consider such things carefully before you choose to embark on the path of change. To be a master can be lonely when you are few and far between. Earth is yet one of the lonely outposts of the system!

Chapter Thirty-Two

"A piece of wood may be saturated with water. Water may in its turn be filled with gas. Exactly the same relation between different kinds of matter may be observed in the whole of the universe: the finer matters permeate the coarser ones." Gurdjieff

"The splitting of the atom has changed everything save our mode of thinking, and thus we drift toward unparalleled disaster." Albert Einstein

Should you choose to embark upon the path of conscious development, your identity will change. You learn that people most commonly identify themselves with concepts and beliefs built upon the shifting sands of emotion. Most of their behavior is motivated by action and reaction to external or internal stimuli that are attached to that shaky belief system.

For example, as a child you may have seen someone react with fear toward thunder or lightning. From that point on, especially if reinforced by other like experiences, you share those fears. Your behavior is based upon that emotion. You remain indoors during an electric storm, rather than outside taking delight in the powers that move through the sky.

With a trained mind using points of reference, you feel fear, acknowledge that you are at level two, and shift if you choose. With practice you need no longer shift levels consciously because you have learned that even human emotion is an illusion. You can now turn emotion on or off at will; it has no control over you. You are a superb actor or actress!

From that point, you discover new feelings that are the true faculties only symbolized by emotion. The gods feel human emotion when they choose. They also know the real meaning and depth of joy and love; and neither has control over them.

As you read these things, listen to the associations that are being made in your mind. Apply these principles within your own discipline and experience. Listen to the still small creative voice that is speaking inside as you read and ponder. Write down your ideas, talk to others about them, try them. . .

For example, if you are a speech therapist working with people who stutter, you may consider that such a person is operating primarily at level three. He or she may be rethinking, reliving what they said and what others said to them during a past verbal exchange, or any other interaction. In effect, such a person is integrating the higher levels of meaning, the between-the-lines messages the other was sending.

Perhaps you could teach them to be aware that their nature spans many levels. When they are having difficulty such as stuttering, they can make a temporary level shift.

It may be that when they stutter they are at level two, through conditioning, operating with awareness centered on fear of rejection, ridicule, failure, embarrassment.

Teach them to recognize that fear as simply a point of reference that they are then at level two, and can shift if they choose. Perhaps lack of self-esteem is founded upon similar fears.

Understand also that some persons may stutter because they are training someone else to communicate at many levels simultaneously; as they do.

Sensitive people are the ones most likely to be labeled society's misfits. No one has taught them that they are different because they are aware of more things at the same time than are most others. Their lack of self-esteem and their peculiar symptoms are only indications that they function more adequately above level one. Pathology may only exist in the minds of those who judge another to be inferior, or superior.

Should you be working with people who have epilepsy or other temporary loss of control over their physical body, you may have concluded that everyone else also *"blinks their eyelids"*; but each at varying rates of speed.

To be on the wheel is to be dizzy. If you spin your body in a circle, you will lose orientation for awhile and display erratic behavior without drugs, alcohol, or mental illness. While you are disoriented, should you spin in the opposite direction you will immediately stop the dizziness and regain your balance.

Could such principles be applied in the mental health field? Could some forms of mental illness be a mind that is spinning too fast or too slow to mesh with consensus choice levels? It may be that the asylum inmate is using fifty percent of his or her brain capacity, while the resident doctor is fixated at four percent!

If you are a physicist, a biologist, a chemist, an astronomer, consider the patterns that repeat themselves from macro to micro worlds; the reverses and mirrors, the illusion of separation. This record is a seed, a seminal vessel bobbing in the rich currents of your own creative imagination.

In the order of planets look for the order of atoms and molecules. Check the rates of spin to determine which governs which, and where the center is. Look for identical governing principles in all relationships.

The master plan is exceedingly clever, but very simple!

In the body of man find the pattern of his mind; the mind of God in his thoughts. Learn for yourself correct principles; and govern your research and thinking accordingly. You may be searching far beyond the mark; lost in a complex maze of ideas that have no foundation in reality. Is it not so that the great discoveries of science are a breakthrough from a complex theory to a simple truth?

Could it be that when the computer has gone through its full cycle, all that has meaning is the process of discovering that it exists? Could the simplest child in an orphanage go up to a matured Einstein and say, *"I could have told you so?"*

Do not some of the things we write stir deep feelings inside your bosom? Do you sometimes feel lost in your world and want to weep as a little child? If you have the desire, you are called and programmed, foreordained from the foundations of this world to that work. Many others are waiting for you to take initiative; to manifest and share that which you most desire, that which you are. . .

Think things through for yourself. We shall not address each discipline. For Kira and I there is only one discipline. We would that all were gentle with each other. Judge no one to be less or greater than yourself. Every individual is a seed bursting to pour out knowledge upon you; if you will suspend judgement, and listen with love. How can you expect to change if you do not do something different?

Listen to the children, the grandparents, the sick and the misfit. Visit those who are in prison and in the hospitals. They are sent to teach you who you are. They may be masters or gods in disguise. With each new relationship you may be confronted with your own *"one cubic centimeter of chance!"*

Chapter Thirty-Three

"Is there any other seat of the Divinity than the earth, sea, air, the heavens, and virtuous mind? Why do we seek God elsewhere? He is whatever you see; He is wherever you move." Lucan, A.D. 39-65

"There is no fear in love; but perfect love casteth out fear. . ." John 4:18

"To the weak became I as weak, that I might gain the weak: I am made all things to all men, that I might by all means save some." 1 Corinthians 9:22

We suggest, should you embark upon a period of development, that you consistently maintain a physical discipline. Drive a car, ride a bicycle, do calisthenics, aerobics. Deliberately do different things at different times. Make it a habit for a while to change your habits. Become a close observer of the physical world and the people around you. This alone will teach you wondrous things.

You can become aware of magic rings by carefully observing patterns of movement around you, and the things that people are saying. You may notice a penny in a strange place; a trail of pennies, a pair of sunglasses on the sidewalk in the night, a green garbage bag where no bag should be, people in strange places doing strange things. Once your eyes are open you needn't be controlled by such operations. You will be aware of those who are.

It is said that the opposite of love is not hatred, but fear. Perhaps all negatives are based on fear. Where fear is, there is no love. Where love is, fear cannot dwell. Are you moving toward something with love as your motive, or are you moving away because of fear?

Sorcerers sometimes apply powerful psychological principles to effect change in their apprentices through fear. The same principles could be used with the reverse motivation of love instead of fear. In the world of illusion, look for the opposite. You are seeing a mirror image until your mind has been trained like a magician.

People who have not trained their mind to be aware of levels and level shifts, see in the external world and in the meaning of words only that which is the prevailing psychology of lower levels. In this way they limit their understanding and the quality of their experience.

A master must then reach for that person at the level of communication where their awareness is consistently centered. This can lead to misunderstanding regarding the motive of the master. The person he addresses judges the master's behavior according to a limited and rigid range of past experience patterns.

Often the master is only able to plant a seed for the future learning of a prospective student, instead of engaging in an intensive teaching/learning relationship, which is the master's desire. People can only be taught at the rate at which they choose to limit themselves.

In this record we have included material which we would rather not wade through, but we must appeal to many different starting points.

You dream of walking in the mud. We reach out for you where you are! Only open your mind and heart and you will be led to a golden book that contains no trivia. Before the new world can come, that golden record must flood the earth and the souls of man. . .

The span of the mind of man is limitless. If you choose to look for my footprints upon the earth, you will find them there. If you choose to look for me in the heavens, there am I also. I am where you are. You are where your awareness is centered. If you see me as a man walking upon the earth, that is where I am for you. Look for me where you prefer to find me. If you would limit your understanding, our relationship, to talking at level one or reading a book, you have your desire.

Where two or more are gathered with one mind for the common purpose of learning, the master is there.

We will teach you a game of learning when you have prepared your mind a bit further. . .

Chapter Thirty-Four

"The most effective kind of education is that a child should play amongst lovely things." Plato, B.C. 427-347?

Close to the everyday awareness of most adults is the perception of a dynamic dreamlike world, an internal movie. These ongoing subconscious stimuli often seem to have little relation to dominant cultural consensus reality. The curious will sometimes tap this movie through hypnosis or meditation.

Sometimes these levels of communication are identified as experiences with past or future lives lived upon this or other planets. Other explanations may include such concepts as the *"akasha"* or the *"collective unconscious"*.

It is not necessary with new age energies to tap these sources with ponderous techniques such as staring at a candle while somebody mutters words to put you in a trance. Hypnotic techniques are effective, but why submit to that when you can be wide awake and aware?

It may be difficult for an individual untrained mind to keep the memory patterns upon one scene for any length of time. Every stimulus is associated with thousands of others in a long chain. The pictures you are tapping may therefore leap from planet to planet, time to time.

We suggest that should you choose to tap these resources, you work initially with two or more people together. One person will act as conductor. A trancelike state is entered by exercising the imagination.

The conductor prompts you to visualize or otherwise sense a butterfly, a bird; or even a blue feather! Your eyes are open or closed. You sit, lie down, or stand; it matters not. What do you see? What color is it? What is it doing? What are you wearing on your feet? Are you male or female? Look around, you may be in another place. Are there people around you? Do you have a relationship with any of the people?

The questions are flexible. The conductor keeps you centered on one scene until it ceases to have significance. You are wide awake. No one controls you more than in your physical state.

With two people sharing an altered state of reality it is easy to awaken other memory patterns which usually, as the conductor gains in skill and confidence, will result in a chain of thinking that will solve some current problem that is bothering you; or will reveal to you that which you most desire in the physical here and now.

You and the conductor have become as little children, playing a game in the sandbox of life. You are giving yourselves permission to be somewhere else than where consensus reality demands. You are beginning to see another's interests as your own, and are validating and sharing another's dream. . .

Chapter Thirty-Five

"For God doth know that in the day ye eat thereof your eyes shall be opened, and ye shall be as gods, knowing good and evil." Genesis 3:5

At some point in your training, you become aware of a power moving upon you like the shadow of some giant spacecraft that blocks out the sun, the moon, the stars, the world. You become aware that you are being taught by an intelligence that knows your every thought, feeling, dream, vision, movement, identity. Your level of intelligence to theirs is less than that of a gnat.

They demonstrate their love, consideration, gentleness, toward an earthworm whose mangled stepped-on body to you shows no sign of life. They show you how that single worm's sacrifice has created the universe within which you live. They toy with your emotions; dangle you like a puppet on a string. They strip away your identity, and the significance of man as you knew him.

Never before had you considered such things. Logic and learning fail you utterly. Your beliefs and sacred experiences are shattered. You are powerless in their hands; you are nothing. You become the mangled earthworm. . .

You are tested and tried to see how far you will go with your sacrifice, your crucifixion. Will you cling to life for an hour, a day, two days, seven if it will save one soul? You are powerless to move; there is no life in your limbs; only a spark of something that communicates with god. Your body is perfectly still; frozen solid like a statue cast in bronze, or a pillar of salt. You believe all things. You accept all things. You are having a close encounter with god. . .

Much later, after you have suffered all things willingly, after you have consented to everything, after you have acknowledged that there must be a greater god; you become aware that another could take up the cross from you, and also needs to have that learning experience. It becomes silly to lie there not moving, clinging to life for another.

Should another be god, and you remain a worm forever? You are learning to balance mercy with justice, sacrifice with being. You are learning to be a god.

You are given all the secrets of the hierarchy. Nothing is withheld. You become like the gods. All entities below hear your voice as the voice of god. Worlds instantly obey your every command; willingly give their all, their life, their suffering, their joy, their pain for you.

They know that you have done so for them.

You know that you are god. You say, *"I am god therefore. . ."*, and you attach your wish, your desire, and it is done. . .

Then the power ceases to overshadow you. As they leave, your heart goes with them. You are one of them now. They have left you alone, abandoned on a world where none other knows what you know. You alone walk as god upon the earth. The former life you knew has become nothing. It ceases to be fun. You experience the pain of pure boredom. You want desperately to be with your own kind; you need desperately to be with your own kind.

As they left, they reminded you that you could go to them. You are god, you can do all things. But a balance must be struck. The only way for you to rise is for another to descend. To realize your own being, another must be sacrificed.

You are god. People have become as worms compared to your level of intelligence. You are walking upon an earth that is populated only with worms. It is a dying, a dead planet. If it were sacrificed, perhaps all could rise with you to a higher consciousness, to where the gods dwell. It means nothing for physical bodies to die. You know that now, you have offered yours.

You begin to ascend, knowing that as you do millions of lives are extinguished. You hear their final collective song. It is a group song, the voice of millions singing together as one. It is a song of gratitude for having known you, a thanksgiving for the blessing of being able to serve you, to give their lives for you; a song of trust, and a hope that you will take them with you.

Only then, when many worlds and millions of lives have already been burned and destroyed by the glory of your passing, do you begin to realize that the higher gods were only testing you. They had demonstrated their love, their consideration for, their gentleness toward a single mangled earthworm. They had shown you the highest attributes of godhood, the true order of the universe. . .

Your new doubt, your guilt, your sudden anxiety fills your pockets with lead weights, heaps coals of fire upon your head, dangles millstones from your neck. The lightning ceases to flow in your veins. You sink down and down, lower and lower, down, down, down, until you strike bottom and can sink no more. You find some cold stone to crawl under, some mountain to fall down upon you to crush your body and hide you from the gods forever.

Yet you remember. Never can you cease to remember. There is no oblivion for you!

The universe holds its breath now. All clocks have stopped; waiting, waiting for you to crawl out from your hiding place; waiting for the sun to shine again, the moon to give her light, the stars to dance together in the night skies; waiting for time and people to be again; children, mothers, fathers, joys, sorrows, good times, hopes, dreams, blue skies; waiting, waiting for you to remember, that you are god!

Chapter Thirty-Six

"Where two or three are gathered together in my name, there am I in the midst of them." Matthew 18:20

We will now teach you a game, a technique for mind expansion. You already know how to play this game, you have already played it. The more you play the more aware you become that you are playing and the more aware you become the easier and easier it gets to play. The easier and easier it gets to play the more you become aware of yourself. The more you become aware of yourself the easier it gets to know that you are. When you know that you are you know that there is a greater god.

We suggest that this technique, this game be played in a dyad. We suggest also that it be one male and one female, a potential God, who have chosen each other as partners.

When you share a dream with another and actually live the experience in its entirety together, bonds are formed in that new dyadic reality that are stronger than any known to physical relationships. You need not enter into the game to that extent perhaps, and can later widen your experience to include others, but the initial attachments may be much stronger suddenly than those you feel for a wife, husband, or emotionally attached other. The new bonds are not likely to wear off in this life even should you choose to look back and attempt to retrace your steps. In effect, you are selecting an awake and aware level three relationship, as opposed to the usual level two bonding.

Nothing happens by accident. The choice of partners will likely represent attractions from premortal life experience.

You begin the game by sitting down facing each other in the same way you used to be taught by the masters. You may choose to imagine a circle of others about you, clothed in robes of white, listening to the master's voice, waiting to feel the soft touch of his hand, the glance of his eye upon the crown of your head.

You may visualize a temple nearby, glowing with a soft white-blue light. Perhaps, if the gates of the courtyard are open, you may catch a glimpse of the inner door, the entrance to the temple.

As you begin to communicate, maintain silence. Observe yourself in the other. Learn again the body language you knew so well before. Look closely at the wealth of expression in each other's eyes and countenance. The eyes are truly the windows of the soul. Watch for the tiny movements of muscles, the lifting of a hand, an arm. Every movement will trigger chains of associations, memories from the past when each of you moved in exactly that same manner before.

Become aware of the whole person before you at once. Feel for the meaning, the thoughts of each other. Look for yourself in the other. Continue to observe closely, childishly; open, trusting, sharing yourself completely on the mental plane; wishing for the other to know the fulness of your thoughts and dreams; wanting to know the fulness of the thoughts and dreams of the other. It gets easier and easier. You have already done this, somewhere in time. . .

You may wish to broaden communication by introducing the magic of words. You need to accept the other's interests as your own. Such an acceptance, seeing the other person as yourself, creates the magic of synergy. The two begin to think as a whole that is greater than the sum of the parts. The two are together with one mind. The master is there.

Formulate the words that come for you. Or use the following as a guideline if you prefer. These words can be spoken aloud by one or the other, or both, watching closely for yourself in the other.

"We move within limitless love and truth. The only rule is: There are many springs and many summers, sometimes it is more fun to just - float!"

"When the teacher is ready, the student appears. The teacher is ready when he accepts another's interests as his own. The student accepts the teacher by seeing his interests as her own. By accepting another's interests as her own, the student becomes the teacher. There are only teachers along the path. Where two or more are gathered with one mind, the master is there."

"The master accepts the teacher by seeing their interests as his own. The teacher accepts the master by seeing his interests as their own. By accepting the master's interests as their own, the teacher becomes the master. When the teacher becomes the master, the master appears. Who am I? Who am I?"

The above could be spoken from memory at each session. Your mind is beginning to expand as it grasps for meaning of basic truths, and as it links completely in the interests of another.

Ensure that each of you is having fun. If at anytime either ceases to have fun, immediately break off the game for a time of integration. Do something else: sing songs, dance, go for a drive, a swim, wash the dishes, take out the garbage, be by yourself. Think out the only rule of the game, and stick to it. Never force another against their choice. Be gentle with each other. It gets easier and easier. . .

Chapter Thirty-Seven

"Consider the lilies of the field, how they grow. . ." Matthew 6:28

The metaphysical community, the sensitives as a network weave a delicate invisible fabric like an intricate golden spider's web over their city. When an unknown being with power steps inside their territory they know and investigate. There is room for one more, but that new one must be probed, credentials examined, intentions stated, before the community can rest secure that their own fabric is safe from harm.

Consider if you will, a new city in a valley, a new network, a new fabric being woven. . .

Through the long dark night the fabric weavers toiled tirelessly at their creation. Fingers flying furiously they hastened their work to completion. None paused to question the rush, each knew their own part must be played perfectly and with haste. Programmed to work with thousands of others in a precise harmony of timing and coordinates, each of the workers knew that a mistake by anyone would leave a hole, an imperfection in their garment. Each rapid movement was precise and careful according to plan. . .

A gathering hush, the unreal sound of silence slowly began to move over the assembly. The fabric weavers had finished their task. The delicate creation, the intricate interwoven patterns, the beautiful scents, the softness of perfection had been realized. The garment was prepared and ready for the bridegroom. The morning of the wedding day was at hand.

They rested then, thousands of them, seated in tiers, ascending rows of circles rising in the form of a wine glass, a chalice that almost closes at the top. They say that some of them, those seated in the sides of the north, looked up and saw outlined against the darkness of the night, strange beings like angels or guards moving slowly in the open space at the top of the chalice.

None knew how the intruder had penetrated the veil. They knew only that an alien being had flashed suddenly through their space and was standing in the center, looking up and around. They sensed his power. Thousands together knew that this one, this alien was greater than them all. They thrilled with the sound of his voice; a still small whisper that penetrated their very being and made their heart leap as one.

He said he was a lightbearer come from the mountains above the dark valley. He said he brought tidings of peace and great joy. The light of the sun had been seen from the top of the mountains. The long promised day was approaching, the wedding feast about to begin.

He sounded a strange sound, a call, a word that had never been heard before. It swelled and filled their whole universe, causing the fabric to ripple and move like waves upon the sea as the word flowed out to mingle with the darkness in the valley, and to bounce and hollow echo from the sides of the mountain outside.

From their midst arose a beautiful maiden. They hadn't noticed her before. They saw that her hands were not worn and aged with work and care as theirs were. They marvelled at her delicate features, the grace of her movements, as she walked to the center and linked hands with the lightbearer.

He seemed to know she would come. They began to dance together. It was a strange peculiar dance, a festival of light that was watched closely with great wonder and curiosity. The couple danced as one, ascending slowly upward in a spiral, a taper, a beautiful harmony of delicate graceful movement. The clasp of their hands never broke. The hands formed a sphere, a perfect sphere. . .

They say that the very first ray of sunlight to enter the valley met them precisely at the peak of their dance. To the fabric weavers, the thousands who watched, it seemed as though the lightbearer and his companion became the beam of sunlight. Those sitting close to the top would say later that the couple were transformed into a perfect pearl, a beautiful delicate pearl that could only have been spun from pure gold.

As the sunlight beamed its warm pleasure upon the valley floor, the new lily for the first time slowly opened her petals wide. The fabric weavers saw then the fulness of their creation. They saw the completeness of her intricate patterns, the colors, the nectar beaded like golden crystals or dewdrops of light wine; the sweet scents of her perfume, the glorious perfection of her delicate fabric.

The gods smiled upon the lily of the valley as they danced at the wedding feast on the tops of the mountains. . .

Chapter Thirty-Eight

During the last quarter of a century, scientific research has been conducted in a field that has been familiar to witches for centuries. Science has secretly discovered that if you take a sample of blood from a man you may then track that person for a lifetime. You know where he is, what he is doing, much of his thinking; and thereby can predict with accuracy what his next movements are likely to be.

He becomes a lifelong mark for experimentation; a vehicle to carry out the designs and plots of the secret powers that be. It may be that many, especially those who have had military or police service, are so marked and tracked.

The methods have evolved and been refined over the years. It may be that now only a single blood cell is needed. Perhaps even a cell from a hair, or a brain cell if available. Each brain cell may be like a hologram, a perfect copy. Regardless of how often it is split, it contains yet the whole of its being.

The medical profession has routine access to all parts of the bodies of its patients. Doctors and technicians often scurry to laboratories with bits and pieces to perform their peculiar witchcraft upon.

Few children are born without a medical expert in attendance. Infants are given routine injections. The doctor believes from his books and the testimony of others that he is doing what is right. No doctor who practices upon patients has the whole key to the purpose of medicine and nutrition. But some are more knowledgeable than others. Could the process of disease and aging be altered?

In Montreal, a man touched by the finger of destiny develops a technique to operate upon the exposed brains of human beings while they lie on the table awake and aware. He discovers that he can map new coordinates by touching the living brain of his patients with an electric probe.

Touch one spot, a hand lifts, and an arm; another and the patient hears music; another, scenes from childhood are relived vividly in living color. The doctor becomes the most famous of neurosurgeons and saves the lives of many.

In his later years, Wilder Penfield will write books about his experiences. He will express his loneliness, his anger at the lifestyle of others around him. *"Save my patients, for what?"* he will explode.

Few are interested in reading his books about the bible and a greater god. He has spent a lifetime probing and operating upon the human brain. But in his last days he senses failure; the failure of science. He has never discovered the mind, the spirit, the missing link. What was he really doing all those years as people trusted their life to his hands, his decisions? He dies without answering the vital questions. . .

From South America comes word of a psychic surgeon who operates upon people with a rusty knife. The incision heals instantly. Others are said to operate with bare hands. The surgeon dies suddenly.

Laser surgery, precise instruments to cut, observe, and manipulate miniscule parts of the human body are developed.

A psychiatrist writes of thirty years living among the dead. He exorcises his hopeless patients with static electricity, then talks intelligibly with the entities who possessed their bodies. He gives them new coordinates, new space, and greener pastures in which to roam and to learn. The patients live and are freed from the asylums where they were imprisoned. At his death the psychiatrist's work is sentenced to the dusty shelves of spiritualist doctrine.

"In the last days you shall do even greater things than I", Jesus tells his disciples near Galilee.

A familiar pattern unfolds. Atlantis and Mu meet at the center. The eagle lands on the moon. The spaceship Columbia sails forth and returns with a sign, an olive leaf from the gods, a replica of that which can only be created among the stars; a sphere, a perfect sphere.

The last bridge is severed, the corpus callosum cut. The brain and the atom are split. The results are in, the coordinates mapped, the timing noted. This time it will not be a practise drill, a dry run!

Chapter Thirty-Nine

"Out of the ground the Lord God formed every beast, and he brought them unto Adam to see what he would call them." Genesis 2:19

"The Lord God caused a deep sleep to fall upon Adam, and he took one of his ribs, and closed up the flesh instead thereof. And the rib made he a woman, and brought her unto the man." Genesis 2:21,22

You are Adam in the garden, naming the animals as the gods bring them to you pair by pair for your inspection and approval. . .

You are learning a new language. Words, magic words move upon the air in the garden for the first time as each animal is given a new name by the splitting of your lips. The sounds swell forth as a breath of air, a mighty rushing of wind from your bosom, the center where the heart dwells.

You learn to breathe then. As you surrender to the magic of creating words, you are emptied inside and fill your soul with the inbreath, the breathing in of the virgin atmospheres of your new world. You have become human. You speak in tongues, breathing out what you are. What you are is changed by the world outside and breathed in as a balm of healing and new delight; only much later to become a bomb of passion, poison, and pollution. Your first breath was perfect, innocent, a gift from the gods. Your second was your own experience, your own operation upon gross matter. The first word was theirs; all others are of your own choosing.

"In the beginning was the Word, and the Word was with God, and the Word was God. And the Word was made flesh and dwelt among us."

The man is not without the woman in the Lord. Adam is lonely in his new world. The gods have not yet brought you your Eve.

You think of other worlds, another time perhaps, when the gods jested. They put you to sleep, opened your side, withdrew a rib, and planted a thorn in its place. You lived with that thorn like a viper in your bosom; and it hurt, it hurt like hell! You wonder if the methods of the gods are more refined now.

You don't trust them. You choose to stay wide awake and aware throughout the operation this time. . .

Chapter Forty

There are two towers in the garden. Each has many levels, many stories, many rooms. In one of them, Wilder Penfield scrubs and gets ready for his patient.

In the penthouse, the chairman turns on all his circuits and sits down, knowing it will be a long screening and many cuts will yet have to be made. A master plan must be conformed to.

Seated in tiers ascending in rows of circles rising in the form of a wine glass, a chalice that almost closes at the top, thousands upon thousands wait breathlessly, watching the garden with its two towers in the center below. They try to peer through the windows that are not draped and veiled, hoping to learn some secret of how the gods multiply. They must wait for a sign, someone to appear on a balcony to give news of the birth, and to say the new name and color.

You are Adam lying on a bed, a table, draped in sterile sheets spun from soft white fabric. Beneath the sheets you are naked. They have shaved your head with a razor, pulled back your scalp, split your skull. Recording cameras whirr softly; circuitry comes to life. The chief surgeon is there.

Strangely you feel no pain, as if bare hands, spirit hands, had entered your body somewhere, everywhere, and you know the incision will heal by itself instantly. The lights are soft overhead. You imagine you see angels, guards perhaps, moving back and forth slowly between you and the ceiling. You relax and let go, you are in good hands. . .

The chief surgeon talks to you, asks questions, maps out the coordinates of your brain; links brain to body. You answer, cooperate fully, volunteer information, sensations, feelings. You trust completely; it must be done perfectly.

How much brain to cut out, how much to leave in, is the question and the balance. The chief surgeon choses for you; makes decisions that will mean life or death; human, animal, vegetable. Or a corpse disintegrating; water, air, mineral. One cancer cell missed will be a time bomb waiting to explode in your brain.

This operation has never been done before. The patient is new, the brain is different, the personality and experience of the surgeon have never before been exactly as at this moment. . .

The pilot found the hare. Without instruments he operated with his bare hands to remove the implant. The coordinates had been burned into his brain with the programming for the mission. He knew it had to be done while the trumpet was still sounding, or the implant would have begun to multiply and to kill the hare. Such a thing had never been allowed to happen before. No animal had ever been sacrificed to propagate the gods.

In hopeless anguish, the pilot took the tiny embryo to his bosom and placed it carefully inside the folds of his garment, next to his heart. The incision in the side of the hare healed instantly. The pilot knew that without his lost instruments he could not check the hare's system to ensure that no alien cell had been left inside. All he could do now was wait, and search the skies. . .

As you lie on the operating table, feeling nothing, the tension of having to lie perfectly still begins to take its toll. You grow weary and sleepy. The lights begin to dim and you wait for someone to slap your face and wake you up. Your hands, your arms are lifeless at your side, you have not power to raise them by yourself. The ceiling somehow begins to move closer and you note for the first time that it has thousands of tiny holes, contours, shapes, forms, shadows. You feel light, strange, peculiar. You wonder if the surgeon has touched another spot with his electric probe and is playing another game with you.

You weep for him. You wanted so much for him to return your trust, to understand your desires, your needs. You trusted him to take you out gently. But you see clearly how they pound on your chest and bloody your lip in their haste to force another breath, an alien breath, into your bosom. . .

In another room somewhere within the two towers, Adam waits for the gods to begin. He has been on the wheel before, he knows what to expect. This time there is no dizziness. He is awake and aware as the critical point is reached and he disintegrates, becomes nothing, again. But he has been there before and it is nothing this time.

They promised you that you yourself would create the most beautiful woman in the universe, for your companion. You trusted them and gave everything willingly, going to your death awake and aware as you had desired. Now as you lie on your bed you know that the operation has commenced. You feel the knife, painless, yet leaving a hollowness in your bosom; an awareness that you are slowly being split in two.

You watch television, knowing that you are powerless to move your legs and your body below the waist. You agreed to the perfect stillness and gave up power over your body. You know the legs will be freed to give you relief when the knife moves up to bisect your chest and spine.

Outside there is silence. Time has stopped. The world has ceased to turn. The people are frozen, pillars of salt lest a breath somewhere disturb the surgeon's knife.

All your training has been for this moment only; the endless days of sacrifice in the body of a mangled rotting earthworm, clinging to a tiny spark of life. The years, centuries, transfixed, crucified on a wheel had purpose and meaning only to train you to perfect stillness, the stillness of death while remaining awake and aware to answer the surgeon's questions.

Atom by atom, cell by cell, an invisible surgeon is splitting you into a perfect pair. For eons of time you have been probed, tested, examined, measured. When you slept, when you blinked your eyes, as you breathed; every movement was closely observed, recorded, entered into the highest computer. There can be no mistake in the cloning of a God. The master cell must be identified with perfect certainty and precision from countless other cells adrift in a universe of worlds, galaxies, systems.

Television has been invented for this moment. Your mind must be distracted from the operation that is taking place.

In living color you watch the entire history of the world unfold before your eyes. You see all movies, all books, all media, all movements, all words that ever were or ever will be spoken upon this planet from its beginning. You select the channel from your bed. As your mind moves and turns, the channel moves and turns. You see not only what is and was but also what could have been. You see where you made a wrong choice, a bad decision, or where someone else interfered with your freedom to choose, played out as if nothing wrong had ever happened.

On the screen you have every desire you ever had fulfilled. You see the end from the beginning, the beginning from the end. When you tire of watching one period of time, you switch channels or turn off the set; it matters not, it's all up to you. You are the master of time and space. You control the television set, another splits your body.

You begin now to think as a pair. Your upper body is frozen, except the lips. You can talk and respond to the questions of the surgeon. Individual cells directly in the line of cut must make choices which way to go. The television is off. Your mind is needed here now, awake and aware.

Since the beginning of time you have been making choices. Each choice was for the purpose of defining the most beautiful woman in the universe. She was choosing the most perfect man. Each choice was for this moment.

All human emotions, feelings, interactions, senses, relationships; every single thing ever created in the universe, was made and moved solely for the purpose of giving the gods the experience they need to decide and choose for themselves the qualities they want for their eternal companion; when they are cloned as God.

Everything that has been written in this book, everything you have ever become aware of at any level since you were created from elemental intelligence, has been for this one purpose only. Nothing else matters; nothing else is real. Only God is real. Only this moment exists.

You become aware now as the operation continues, that you are reviewing your life on earth. All relationships, all links, all associations, all connections are being renewed and remembered.

A question is asked. Half of you responds with half the answer, the other half of you completes it. A key name must be given as the answer to each question. Half of you gives the first name, the other half the surname. You are judging the people whose names are given; picking and choosing your own, those you would have dwell with you forever.

Sometimes only half of the answer is given. At those times you know the surgeon is testing, probing his map, his coordinates, asking trick questions, playing games designed from the beginning to ensure there are no mistakes made through deception and guile. All language has been invented for this purpose.

A white eagle flies over the surface of the earth, swiftly from place to place as associations are given, names spoken aloud. The eagle undoes the magic, the karma, the misunderstandings. Your slate is being cleaned completely. The garbage of the gods must be taken out; no trace of your having walked among the people as one of them can remain.

At times you sense that all systems are being tested: sight, sound, touch, taste, smell, sex, others. Questions elicit strange words in a preprogrammed map that tells the surgeon precisely where the knife is at, exactly which cell is responding.

The split, the cloning, never ceases. Your life continues to be reviewed, faster and faster as the white eagle gains experience and brings more characters upon the stage.

The purpose of living has been to provide the associations, the words, the magic words that the surgeon needs to hear to know that everything is unfolding as it should. He is looking for, waiting to hear, the final word, the word that will tell him it is finished.

You sense the rings of power that are moving in response to each operational level at which you are tested. As you move to lower levels the white eagle takes over. He constantly returns to gently request your permission to probe deeper and deeper. You uncover some sins, some stains, some dark spots in your development. Again in his gentle way the white eagle seeks your assurance, asks if you are willing to go deeper yet. The choice is yours. All powers move to fulfill your desire. You are in good hands.

When you get too deep the arc ascends again. Like a flowing sine wave, it moves up and down to keep you awake and aware without trauma or pain, yet penetrating high and deep enough to reach the bounds of perfection.

Later, when the lower depths have all been explored and the eagle has flown throughout the world to touch every single person, every memory bank you have ever had an effect upon; you see him with his ring sweep the earth and map new coordinates, a new navigational system to replace the old which had become polluted. You see their excited victory roll, an outside loop in perfect formation, and hear the white eagle's exultant whistle. The mapping is complete beyond all expectations, beyond all hopes and dreams.

You thank them as they fly to the west, their mission complete, a well-deserved rest and renewal at hand. All parts have been played to perfection. It was a good gain!

Soon after the new map is drawn, you begin to take over from the surgeon. The two of you are now at the controls. You are creating each other.

You aren't sure just where the knife is cutting now. You feel as though your entire body is split in two. But the invisible knife is still there. You can sit up now. You see your reflection in the mirror. You see only a perfect man.

You listen without ears as fine tuning is done. You hear an unspoken question from your companion. The pace is slower now, much slower. You answer with a decision, an approval to action: *"Yes, that will work." "Yes, that is correct."*

Your mind is pure logic. You analyze everything totally; knowing all connections, all channels, all conduits, all associations. A perfect psychology is considered for all levels. You know everything. You are God. . .

You sense then the struggle that has taken place in your body as cells rushed frantically to beat the knife and to take their place forever as male or female. You know that previously you were both. Only Gods are pure male and pure female. All other entities are in training, making choices to be either one or the other sex.

You know that the knife moved beyond each point only after all choices were in, all cells in the proper half. Even then there was a question of dominance. Which half would be the greater god?

Your unbroken stream of consciousness has always surrendered to the acceptance of either; yet desired by choice to be male.

The surgeon knew the key to identification and separation of each cell. He knew which cells were touched on the one hand, and which on the other. Any cell which attempted by force or guile to be dominant, was part of the female body. Any cell which was willing to sacrifice everything for the perfection of God, was male.

There were other cells who sat on the fence; not being intelligent or exercised enough to make a complete choice for themselves. It was not until the male and female God were complete and the dominance settled that you became aware of these other spurious cells, and why the knife had not completed its final cut.

The question of dominance was settled by the key programming, the final decision-making power being demonstrated by the master cell. Approval came before action, the thought before the deed.

You felt that the operation was over, finished. Yet you saw that you were still only male in the mirror. You felt they had left a single strand of cells, the heartstring, to join you together yet as one.

The heartstring was a delicate thread like a miniature wedding band, or a crown formed with a priceless pearl, a perfect pearl, and jewels with the colors of the rainbow. You were told that the one you loved the most had the key to your heartstring. You were told that when that one appeared, your heart would leap within and burst the string, the final link that kept you from holding your bride in your arms.

She was yet a shadow inside. You were a shadow to her. But your worlds, your space had been created together. All was in place for the final catalyst. The timing was still in the hands of a greater God.

You wondered if you would ever reach a complete relationship, a consummation with your companion. But you'd been wondering that for eons of testing, thinking all along that *"this time"* would be the last rehearsal. You got up, tottered around a bit, ate something, went back to bed to rest. And it started all over again! It was impossible to handle. The wheel started to spin, you got dizzy. . .

Then you realized that you were simply becoming aware of another aspect of the operation that your mind had been deliberately distracted from. You became aware that you had been operated upon by more than one surgeon. There may have been thousands!

They had been cutting out all the spirit children, the increase you and your companion would ever have. They were cutting them out from your body. You were being tested and tried constantly to see how much of yourself you were willing to give up that others might be. The risk was clear. How much could be cut out without reducing you below the level of a God? It had to be a perfect balance between sacrifice and being. The choice was yours all along; it was your move, your game. That is why you were awake and aware. . .

There is a plan, a reason, a higher meaning for everything. Nothing happens by accident. There is a perfect master plan.

In another room somewhere within the two towers, Doctor Penfield is ecstatic. At last, at last he has found the missing link! He knows now why he had lived his life as he did. He thought all along that he had been operating only on people's brains. To his death he had searched for the human mind, the spirit, the soul; and had never found it. To his death he didn't know that in another room, at a higher level, he had been the chief surgeon of a perfect team who were operating, on the brain cell of a God. . .

The psychiatrist's ring are mobilized to clear the millions of new creations, the new spirit children, eternal dyads in light bodies, from the vehicle of the new God. Together the new dyads are like a flowing sheet, a white blanket of pure electricity driven out to populate the space, the new worlds created for them in a new star system, that would come of age and physical manifestation only when the heartstring of its God was broken.

Now from the room above, through the ceiling you hear the sound of the scraping of a chair being pushed back; the sound of someone rising from a long sitting. Somewhere a car engine starts, then another, and another. People frozen like statues of salt come to life, move, yawn, smile, go about their business. . .

Epilogue

We trust before you leave that you will clean up your space; take an air hose and water to the attic, take out the rugs, vacuum the carpet, polish the mirrors and windows, take out the garbage, close the drapes, pay your bills, let the cat out; and leave a little light burning in the doorway.

As this book is received and applied, so shall be measured the success and the worth of the dolphin project. Marlan and Kira have lived this book. We hold our breath now for you to write the sequel. Please, let's play again. Only this time, make it bigger and better than ever before!

Somewhere, the Unknown God gets up from his bed. He catches a glimpse of himself in the mirror; turns off the television, shuts the closet door, sits at his typewriter; and writes:

The Final Word
If you give me a name, your eyes may see me with that feeling.
If you give me an age, your mind may know me with that much energy.
If you give me a personality, you may think you know me.

Allow me to be nameless, and to be ever changing.
Allow me to be ageless, and to live in this moment.
Allow me to be nondescript, and to melt into your needs.

If you feel you must age me, let my age be forever.
If you feel you must name me, let my name be Love.
If you feel you must know me, know me as Yourself...

(Author Unknown)

If *The Dolphin Project* is not in your local bookstore, additional copies are available from the publisher. The "*golden book*" (550 pages) mentioned by Marlan is also available at the same price. Please send $6.95 per book plus $3.00 shipping and handling each order to:

Sunspring Book Sales
P.O. Box 858
Raymond, Alberta
Canada T0K 2S0